Not About Money

By

Ellen Marie Blend

To Jackie —
a pleasure to
meet you and
share the day at the Reading Festival.
Ellen Marie Blend

i

Not About Money

A LeasCon Book

Copyright © 2001 by Ellen Marie Blend

Copy edited by Pamela M. Green
Associate Editor Toni Rodgers

Library of Congress Number: 2003101047

ISBN: 978-1-929219-05-6

First printing: November 15, 2005

Photograph of General Motors Building – Detroit
obtained with permission from Alexander Media LLC,
National Press Building, Washington, D.C. 20045

Public Notification:
All names of persons have been changed to protect the
privacy of those cited and to avoid any ensuing
controversies.

Screenplay registered with WGA East #136837
Screenplay registered with WGA West #948594

Copies of this book may be obtained through major
bookstores or website http://www.ellenblend.com.

Acknowledgment

I would like to acknowledge all of my many friends and acquaintances of General Motors who so willingly assisted me in my plight against an unruly giant. I would also particularly like to acknowledge two very important people who assured my success; namely, my friend Gail Rubens, whose constant love and expertise were infallible—and my attorney, Dwight Teachworth, whose practices were credibly above reprehension and his approach, opportune recollection of facts and people deservingly notable. I am proud to say that I have a dear and lasting friendship with them both.

Preface

After working an entire career to obtain a much sought after management level, Ellen Blend is victimized and loses her position. Although the bulk of emotions do go out to her, other important elements come into play. The unequal opportunity of restitution for men who are similarly mistreated, the impact on the children of a single mother, and the inconceivable conflicting statements of deponents under oath give this story palpable credence. While each character is notable onto themselves, the reader cannot help but feel contempt for the representatives of a compassionless corporation.

Having said this, a far deeper message should be conveyed. While my story is only one of thousands that could be told, it truly represents reasons for the ongoing demise of Corporate America. It is because of the actions of insensitive corporations over the past decade that there is no more loyalty by employees, no long tenure of workers, and a general attitude of working for a paycheck and not the good of the company.

While situations such as this presented themselves in corporations across the U.S., and devastated countless families, the affect on the upcoming generation is lasting. Ask any young person today how long they will be working for the company for which they are employed, and their answers range from "until I can make more money elsewhere" to "I'm just going to get the rest of my education paid for here, then move on."

Big corporations no longer take care of their employees with health care, retirement plans, and mostly, job security. The payback is in the attitude of American workers today; thus the deterioration of Corporate America.

Introduction

While this story conveys messages that may very well seem that I have a personal vendetta against General Motors Corporation, that is simply not true. I have many great things to say about the corporation as a whole, as it is the true embodiment from which I was formed. I grew up in that corporation and enjoyed many formative years of experiences, education, cultural refinements and, most of all, monetary gains. I truly could not be in a position to appreciate the status that I have attained or live the comfortable lifestyle that I enjoy today without having been a part of General Motors. For that I am both appreciative and thankful.

I did not always feel that the members and management of the corporation acted as an intelligent body, and in the later years of my career to the present time, feel that its actions are that of an ill-fated instrument. The elements of this story are prime examples of what I personally termed "corporate stupidity." This is not an ailment of one corporation. It is widespread among much of big business today, as they struggle in panic to survive in a competitive worldwide market.

For me, the mere circumstances that precluded ending my career successfully with General Motors ultimately gave me an omnipotent framework that clearly embossed my true character.

Victory Party

In appreciation, Ellen Blend held a victory part for all those who supported her throughout the case or privately stood behind her cheering.

CONTENTS

Part I

Chapter One

The Beginning of a Stable Career

It was a cool September day, and I was in school. This was my last year of high school, and I was eagerly awaiting notification of whether or not I had been hired for a co-op job for which I had interviewed. A school co-op program allowed a student to go to school in the morning and work for a company in the afternoon, thus giving work experience and a better education for the future.

The interview I had was in May and with a large automotive company. Many months had passed, including the months of my summer vacation. That was probably the *last summer vacation* I would have, I thought; but no word had come at the start of the school season this late September day.

I was sitting toward the center of the classroom, slightly fidgeting in my chair. I was sixteen years old, timid, and often overshadowed by others. I listened to the announcements being made of some of the students in my class as they were being placed at one company or another. I was worried that I did not get the job. It had, afterall, been several months since the interview. I knew that I was one of three girls that had been sent to General Motors, and I expected that the other two girls also had high scholastic achievements.

I reflected upon the interview I had with General Motors. The man I interviewed with, Mr. Luxem, was cordial but firm. He knew that this was to be my very first real job. His looks reminded me of Soupy Sales.

I had been sent into a very large room with many others for a typing test on some well-aged, rickety typewriters; they were so old that many of the keys had been covered with white bandage tape. I also took a shorthand test, but really could not conceive of how shorthand would work in a real office. Dictation was only a word that I understood, not its true applicability in the business world.

Within the next couple of days, most of the students had been placed in jobs. They were attending class every morning and departing for work in the afternoon. I had already given up on hearing anything on the job for which I had interviewed, but didn't know what else might be available for me. It had already been four months, and I felt that was probably too long to wait to hear something. Maybe the co-op teacher had another place in mind to send the other two girls and myself who had interviewed at the same time.

Finally, word came. I listened intently as I heard my name and the names of the other two girls who had interviewed with the same company.

I was to report on September 16 to the General Motors building in the Chart and Typing Department on the 8th floor. One of my other classmates, Amy Fergeson, was also to report, but to the basement in the Data Processing Department. I felt a little envious, as that sounded so interesting and professional. The third interviewee, Roberta Goodwin, was not hired for a co-op assignment at General Motors. She had been placed in a position with Harper Data, and we were told that she had already started working there.

Mrs. Gordon, my teacher, was a pretty, well-dressed woman of about 30 years old. Her job was to place all of the co-op students with reputable companies for the school year. She asked the two of us to come up to her desk to get our assignments.

We clumsily made our way to the front of the classroom, partially in shock over the news. Our eyes became focused on the paperwork, and our expressions were all agape.

I learned that I would spend the first six months in the chart room, drawing and typing, and then would move on to the typing section of the department. I was quite proud to have been placed at such a prominent corporation.

Chapter Two

Learning to Look Out for Myself

Amy and I rode the bus together from school to work and home, and sat side-by-side toward the back half of the bus. It was the end of the school year, and I didn't know quite how to approach the subject about my being asked to work full time at the end of the co-op term. Being so excited, I knew that I must tell my friend.

I was disappointed to learn that Amy was not asked to stay on. She would be let go at the end of the assignment. How lucky I now felt. My envy of my friend working in Data Processing quickly vanished.

I grew to like my co-workers and leaders very well and formed a comfortable bond with them. After one year, my supervisor, Mr. Waters, called the group up to his desk and announced that he was moving on to a new position. He was a slender man of about 40 with short, light-colored hair. He was quite professional and very pleasant. I liked him very much.

I knew at that moment that I should not get that attached to the people I worked for because they move on. I knew now, in this adult world, that what I needed to do was to look out for myself. I shouldn't stay in one place too long just because it's comfortable—it changes.

That was to be my cue. I was to learn all too quickly that the corporation was dynamic. One of my favorite bosses had found another job and would be moving into his new position, leaving the staff behind. I knew that

5

others would also look to better themselves and would leave a similar void in my corporate family network. I would have to look for other opportunities myself as time went on; I would have to take the lead and look out for myself or be left behind.

As time went on, I also moved into other jobs and earned the respect and admiration of my supervisors and peers. I was frequently loaned out to other offices, and sometimes to the executive staff. I found that I was clearly being groomed for an executive secretarial job.

Chapter Three

Moving Up the Corporate Ladder

Seven years later, I married. At twenty-three years of age, I was a perfect size 5, and my dress and shoes were always completely color coordinated.

When I became pregnant and was scheduled to take a maternity leave, Personnel began sending in girls for my replacement. My current manager, Mr. Kozac, called the personnel office after one of the interviews. He railed at them about the kind of person he was looking for to replace me.

The interviewee, Miss Munson, appeared wearing a short, black skirt, sheer blouse, and shiny white, high-heeled patent-leather boots. Her handbag was quite large, made of clear plastic, and was adorned with white daisies at the base of the interior. The contents of the handbag were primarily exposed.

After Miss Munson had been properly escorted out, Mr. Kozac made a call to Personnel. He made it perfectly clear how he felt.

"Don't you understand the kind of person I've had working for me?" he said. "Ellen is professional, dresses exceptionally well, is clean, neat, and an excellent worker. She can represent me anywhere. Don't send me the kind of person who just left my office. Don't waste my time. I haven't seen one person yet who could replace what I have right now, and that's what I want."

A few other words followed to close the conversation. Mr. Kozac's blood pressure eventually came down, and his red face returned to its normal color. I was secretly pleased that my hard work had resulted in such a positive reputation.

After having two children, I returned to the working world at the end of a year and a half leave of absence. I took it upon myself to move up the corporate ladder about every two years. My level with the corporation changed as well. I received constant raises of substantial amounts in support of my success. I sent in formal suggestions to the suggestion plan and won several awards. My bosses approved of my work and behavior and spoke of me in high regard.

Before reaching mid-career, secretarial work had actually come to bore me. I could type faster than anyone else, made few mistakes, and my English and grammar were excellent. My filing methods were above satisfactory, my accuracy in scheduling meetings and travel arrangements here and abroad were superior, and I had nothing else to learn. I knew that I must move on to different work to satisfy my own needs. I periodically experienced what I termed a personal renaissance where I needed to learn and grow, and this was one of those times.

It was appraisal time, and I was to document my accomplishments, concerns, and future goals on the forms therein. I was now thirty-one and quite confident about my work. I made an appeal to my current manager to move into an analytical position. I didn't actually make it in the normal way, however. Being timid, I decided to express my feelings in the comments section of the appraisal form as follows:

> *I have beaten all records for typing letters, documents and manuscripts. I can schedule meetings and make state-to-state and international travel arrangements flawlessly. My supervisor is so thorough in his filing direction that he doesn't require me to even think. While I enjoy the job assignment, I need a more challenging position.*

I am sure that the comments therein brought an immediate call by Mr. Thompson to Mr. Denver of Personnel. It was agreed that it was probably time that I get some assistance in getting ahead beyond the limits of the secretarial field.

My ability for the technical was abundant, and I could not be contained much longer. Mr. Thompson's inquiry to Personnel brought forth information on a corporate program to help advance persons with both aptitude and motivation. I was there. He found that the corporation would support a program called Salaried Employee in Training (S.E.I.T.), in which a supervisor could elect to send an employee to school for classes of his choice in order to prepare them for a specific job. This program could assist me in moving from secretarial to analytical, and this type of movement was not a normal transition.

Mr. Thompson was a tall, nice-looking man with a cool disposition. He was quite intelligent, but not exactly who you would call Mr. Charisma. He was a man of few words and usually preferred not meeting with you face-to-face. Most of the time I received my assignments by finding them on my chair when I returned from lunch. In retrospect, his conduct wasn't much different from mine.

He suggested the availability of an Employee-In-Training program to me, but said that I would have to wait until a suitable candidate presented herself for my replacement. The time seemed to drag on and on. A well-skilled employee wanted my job, but Mr. Thompson did not want her as a secretary. He told me to please be patient until that person was placed elsewhere. There seemed to be some personality differences, but a stronger possibility was that she was quite unattractive.

He asked what I was enjoying learning in school. I explained that while my current classes did not involve heating and cooling that I was very interested in solar heating. I had been seeing a lot of solar-panel exhibits at school, and I knew that some of our people were working on alternative heating sources as well.

Yes, he agreed that they were. He then shuffled through some papers on his desk to find an example for me. Handing it to me, he said let's see how you do with something more technical. He told me to take the example and to write a technical paper on solar heating. I should return my report in about a week.

I was only too happy to attend the outdoor exhibits of solar panels and other solar heating systems on the school campus grounds. I busily took notes and made sketches for my paper. I don't recall any specific comments, but I turned in my report and believe that he was generally pleased with my work.

Mr. Thompson explained the S.E.I.T. program as one that would allow me to go to school during working hours and to take a couple of classes that were selected by him. He knew that I had been going to school because he approved my tuition refunds; so he asked me to pick up a catalog from the community college that I was already attending.

"You'll have to be patient, though," he reminded me. "It may take a while. As soon as I find a suitable replacement for you, you can be put on a rotational program to do more analytical work. You'll spend three months each with a supervisor in different areas, and I'll try to select courses that will apply for each type of work that you will do. When you have completed the year successfully, you can then be promoted to an Analyst."

He ended our meeting with these comments:

"Hey, I just want you to know. This isn't a program for just anyone who wants it. It is strictly for employees whose supervisors recommend them. An employee must be endorsed by their supervisor and the supervisor must initiate the action. I just want you to know how happy I am to support you on this."

When the undesirable candidate was placed, finally an official search began for my replacement. The ideal applicant arrived for interview, and I soon trained her to relieve me of my current duties. She was not only quite bright and very motivated, she was gorgeous—a delicate lady who was recently married and did not recognize how pretty she was.

Two classes were selected for me by Mr. Thompson. One was a computer class, which began at 8:00 a.m., and the second class was Algebra, thought to be suitable for engineering, at 10:00 a.m. This left an hour gap in my schedule. I gladly enrolled in both classes, but filled the hour gap and my lunch hour with two other classes to accomplish my goal of an Associates Degree more quickly. I was anxious to become equal with my peers, some of whom already had double Masters Degrees.

At the end of my one-year program, I was promoted to become a worthy sixth-level Analyst. I had not quite finished my degree and was disappointed that I had not. Mr. Thompson was still supportive saying that in this way I would get two "hoorahs" instead of one. I would be congratulated now, and then again when I completed the Associates Degree program. I acknowledged his caring with deep appreciation.

I knew that I still had a long way to go, but the only way was up. I had hired in as a third-level Clerk Typist, and had now moved up, grade by grade, to become a sixth-level Analyst.

Chapter Four

Economic Downturn

The years ahead brought much additional learning, and corporate movements and economic downturns brought cutbacks at the corporation. People were being laid off or forced into positions that were not quite suitable for their backgrounds. Times were getting difficult, and the need for change was imminent. Setbacks were ahead, but were thought to be temporary.

This economic downturn brought hard times and forced me out of my engineering job and into an accounting position. I was now thirty-six years old.

David Cantor, a bright, young associate and my current boss, sat in my office one day and talked with me casually. It was 1980. He explained that things weren't looking very good around there, or for the whole corporation, in fact. He explained that there would be a lot of layoffs, and some people were going to be forced into other jobs. He didn't think that I would get laid off because I had too many years in, but he might not be able to protect me in holding my current job.

The next time we talked, he approached me about an interview being set up for me in the Accounting Department. He could see my disappointment as I told him I really had no interest in doing that type of work. He said he was afraid of that, and then tipped me off.

"It's too bad, because Francie Cains would love to work in Accounting; and because of having an uncle on the

Board of Directors, they're probably going to make a position for her here in Engineering.

"Well that doesn't sound fair at all!" I exclaimed. "Why don't they send her to Accounting and let me stay here?"

"When I suggested that, they told me that there really wasn't going to be a position open here," he said.

"Oh! But they can make one for her?" I uttered.

"She's got connections, you know." He was being honest.

Having made an appointment, a more aggressive Ellen marched into the Personnel Office to state my claim to Mr. Denver and make my opinion known.

"I understand I'm being pushed out of my job and maybe into an accounting position, while Francie Cains would like to work in Accounting and they're making a job for her in Engineering."

"Is that what you heard?" Mr. Denver asked.

"Yes, and that's just plain nepotism!" I scowled.

"I know, I know. You're absolutely right. And I don't blame you for being so hot over this. I'll tell you what I'm going to do. Give me twenty-four hours, and I'll make it right," he said.

"What are you going to do?" I asked.

"You'll see what happens. I can't make a job for you in

Engineering, but I can see that she doesn't get one either," he assured me.

Francie Cains didn't get the job, and I was forced to take the accounting position. The mentality of the Accounting Manager was such that he only wanted persons in his group that had finance as their life-long goal, which I did not. That made for an uncomfortable arrangement, and I dragged myself into work each day to perform the duties of my job as Corporate Auditor.

I worked diligently using speed as my challenge. Crunching numbers did not have the same mental stimulation to me as the analytical parts of my engineering jobs. No matter how fast I performed, or how many invoices and travel expense reports that I processed, the boss was never going to approve of me. He continued to give me mediocre appraisals for my efforts. I looked for other opportunities.

Mr. Grainer, my supervisor, was shocked when a request came in for me to interview for a Process Engineering position. It would be entry-level management, one level higher than I already was.

My eyes fell to the first page of the official request. I was excited about the prospect of a new job and getting out of Accounting. I was also especially excited and smug about being sought after for an entry-level management job! I would be a seventh-level employee.

I interviewed for the position, but before it could be consummated, a hiring freeze took place and it could not be offered. The whole job market tightened up. In checking with Personnel, it seemed that the only way to move to a new position was to be laid off and be available for an opening; it was not going to happen through a transfer.

When the announcement came that there would be two people laid off in the Accounting Department, I pretty much knew that I would be one of the persons selected; so, I made it known that I would be willing to go.

I never really regretted that action, but could have if a timely re-hire had not taken place. I had been informed that I could remain on lay-off for a period of one year; but, if I had not been placed within that year, my employment would result in a quit; I would have no recourse. I was not a gambler, but I sure wagered all I had on that move. In actuality, I really didn't have a choice.

I contacted an outside concern that I had worked with while in my previous engineering position, and offered my services as a volunteer. This would give me the ability to make new business contacts and perhaps find other employment. I was not feeling that I had to depend on General Motors to re-employ me. In fact, I felt it would be an opportunity for me to look elsewhere.

I did manage to get a casual job offer from Albert Kahn, an architectural firm, but the interviewer told me that he was not able to offer me nearly the same salary to which I had become accustomed. I held out. It was near the end of my one-year period before another opportunity arose, and when General Dynamics offered me a position within the same salary parameters, I was glad to take it.

Before I actually reported for this position, however, the same job that I had been considered for previously with General Motors opened up. The offer was made, and I preferred to be re-employed with General Motors as the work described in the interview had been more desirable. I took the job and was now a seventh-level employee of the corporation.

I was also most fortunate because I would have lost many years toward a retirement package that only companies like General Motors could offer their employees. In the latter years of my employment, I learned to fully appreciate what my earned pension could do for me.

Other changes were to take place in my life as well. I had been unhappily married for a few years now, but was insecure about filing for divorce without employment. While my husband had filed first and then retracted the suit, I filed later; and then we tried to reconcile. I was still unhappy, and now I could file for divorce again since I had a secure job. While the entire divorce took nine years and five filings, I finally succeeded. It was the right thing to do.

Tony Gallo, an admiring male co-worker, stood at my office door one day waiting for me to go to lunch. He was a medium-height, average-build sort of guy that I considered my friend.

I was now working on my Master's Degree, having time on my hands, and I was always looking to better myself. A comment came from Tony that I never let escape me. It fit comfortably, and I considered wearing it for life.

"You never boast about anything that you do, yet you constantly move yourself forward," he said. "I'd say that you are 'quietly aggressive'!"

I couldn't help but recall a previous supervisor coming to my defense about my leadership position and quiet nature. He told the complainer that while others were making a lot of noise about their responsibilities, I was getting the job done.

"So that's what you call it," I said.

"Yeah, 'quietly aggressive.' I never see you a part of any women's organizations or speaking out for women's rights."

"You're absolutely right. I detest those organizations. I don't feel that I need them to get ahead. I feel that I'll make it on my own merits."

He agreed that I would.

The economic downturn was affecting the corporation immensely. It was chipping away at what was once a healthy, wholesome environment in which to work. At some point in the early eighties, I wrote part of an editorial. At the beginning of the nineties, I revised it as follows:

General Motors Today

While my Christmas decorations remain up at home during the last of the twelve days of Christmas, I have returned to work to be reminded of the absence of what General Motors was many years ago.

The lobby of the General Motors Building was adorned with several magnificently decorated trees, reaching tall to the ceiling. Fresh flowers were placed in the flower boxes at each elevator. The bustling of people filled with holiday spirit, the Goodfellow dolls dressed by GM women, and the singing of carols in the lobby on the day before Christmas, are vacant but in the memories I no doubt share with many others of long tenure.

Today, now residing at the GM Technical Center, aside from the extremely limited decorations, even the normal building upkeep raises an eyebrow. Morale lies low, spirits lag, and still the work continues. Rumors spread of cutbacks in this area and that. Some lost their jobs. Some were pushed into new assignments. Who quit? Where are they going? Surprise after surprise. The growth industry of yesterday lives no more. Survival, surrounded by decay, is GM today.

A walk through the building shrieks the truth of the spirit in the air. On the wall-size "people philosophy," a black magic marker sprawls the word "bullshit." The next corridor has a framed picture of a concept car hung on the wall. A fly has worked its way inside the frame and remains dead under the glass. The restroom sink has been plugged for many days, and water sits in the bowl half way up. The brown paper, which replaced what used to be white, in the towel rack is empty at one end of the room; the paper in the other dispenser is jammed. Some days the brown paper overflows the discard bin and lays on the floor until the cleaning crew shows up.

Standing outside an office where the GM "Mark of Excellence" sign hangs, I wait for the boss to become free. I note that the sign has been mounted on styrofoam. The board has not been squared, but has been cut diagonally so that the back edge protrudes on one side larger than the picture. Studying the sign, I notice that not one side of the sign has been cut straight to match the boarder on the "Mark of Excellence" emblem. Do they not know what excellence is? I then say to myself, this is General Motors today.

Chapter Five

Some Rain Must Fall

These were the best years of my employment with General Motors. I had been given more leniency in my position and more respect than I had ever obtained before. I traveled at will, with assigned job expectations, and not to exceed my personal desires. It was wonderful experience, and it broadened me in a way that only such independence and money can do. I had much to learn in the field of automobiles and did so with exuberance and the support of the staff. I took whatever added training was available to me and went on to finish my education with a Masters Degree. I had worked very hard for my achievements, and was comfortable in my current position.

As life would have it, changes were again to take place. As I once heard, you can always expect change except from a vending machine. The corporation was now to experience the start of a major reorganization that would continue to erupt and reorganize itself over and over again into the millenium. It was the beginning of a down-spiraling effect from which it would never recover.

It was as if all facets of the corporation had been put into a huge mixing bowl, and had been churned up and mixed up to the point of adnauseam. Nothing seemed to work right again. Informal processes that had once worked well with inherent cooperation now failed. Contacts were all changed; persons were in unfamiliar jobs and in unfamiliar territories. Consultant's expertise had rearranged theories and practices until nothing was again recognizable or workable. Work was done to make new procedures, not automobiles.

Acronyms and key phrases abounded, but did little to affect the real business at hand. The "program of the month" became touted among the personnel as some begrudgingly attended new training programs over and over again. Satisfying the plans of the consultants seemed to be the order of operandi, and the engineering and building of automobiles took a back burner. Profits narrowed, executive bonuses dwindled, and the corporation was in a mess. Reorganization again seemed to burst forth, and still there seemed to be no continuity within the old regime as it once had been.

I was transferred to Cadillac, one of three distinct divisions of the corporation that had been divided by locality. While there was some apparent confusion of there being work to do there, after three months I was finally assigned by my new group leader, Mr. Walsh, to be part of a team to reduce production hours at one of the assembly plants. Mr. Walsh was a dignified, nice-looking, PR-type for whom I had respect. My immediate boss was an impudent, afraid-you-might-succeed ahead of him, temper-fit child. I was glad to get away from him by working in another location.

It seemed that this assembly plant was having great difficulty making production on time. They were paying their people a lot of overtime unnecessarily and needed help getting production hours down. I was assigned to the Body Shop and to improve processes that included anything that involved materials. That meant the location of material in the plant, the way in which it arrived, where it was stored, and how it was brought out to the plant floor at the production line. It also included how much workstation stock was required per hour, where it was placed in the work area, how it was placed in the container, its quality, and how the operator used it.

The assignment was both exciting and challenging. Furthermore, the type of work was perfect for me. I had the opportunity to use my architectural skills by sketching out areas of the plant, and placing equipment in layouts which were more efficient and convenient for assemblers. I became an efficiency expert in my own right. I walked around with my clipboard and drawing pencil, climbed up ladders and scaffolding in the plant, and perched myself high above the plant production to view the operation below.

My recommendations to the plant staff heads were generally accepted. Making the actual rearrangements were not always successful, however. Sometimes I would have equipment moved into place before leaving the plant in the evening; but by morning, the night shift had rearranged the floor to suit themselves. Some changes I won on, but on others it was easier to please the workers. They would deliberately and artfully work very slowly if they were dissatisfied, and they had the union there to back them up. Some things you just learned to get along with.

All in all, it was the most rewarding job I ever had with the corporation. I was able to reduce the Body Shop workday from ten to eight hours per day to make the production they needed. And don't you let anyone tell you that a plant job is demeaning. A production environment is quite extraordinary, exhilarating, and personally rewarding. The first-line supervisors were by far some of the sharpest beings with whom I had ever worked.

When that assignment ended, I was again placed in the hands of the controlling supervisor who was afraid you would get recognition. I didn't care for my home-base work location in a bad area of Detroit and cared less for my bully-type manager. I worked hard to find employment elsewhere within the corporation and eventually succeeded.

As luck would have it, it was not too long before the undesirable manager soon followed to be my boss again. The entire staff mirrored my sentiments. Some of the workers actually repositioned their cubicle walls to not leave him an entryway, and hung signs on the walls that said, "The floggings will continue until morale improves!"

Years of tumultuous operations finally showed some improvement, and new systems and procedures became awkwardly workable. Work efforts were now appearing to achieve some forward progress, and the years of failing quality and sales began to level off to a sustainable level. Insignificant profits were massaged in order to appear minimally acceptable to stockholders, and disgruntled employees bantered among themselves how the unclassified were unjustly rewarded despite their failings.

When the gloom began to lift, a change was being made in the personalities of persons who were put into managerial positions. It seemed that the more rash and brazen the character, the more they were rewarded for leadership qualities. Personality tests were given to management and subordinates alike, and only those who fell into the leadership quadrants were praised.

I fell somewhere in the third or fourth quadrant of the personality test in being someone who a great liaison person or ambassador. And yes, there were a select few managers who sat firmly in the same quadrant as myself in the personality tests. They were the nice guys!

Part II

Chapter Six

My Demise

I was now in a planning and timing capacity and was to manage a newly created process. This process was the creation of a very detailed brainchild of the corporation, who painfully documented each and every step that was required to take place from a vehicle's inception to production. I was to manage the timing of the events. I had great empathy for those who could not meet the time frames of the plan. I also saw the ridiculous extra work that had been placed upon people to do detailed write-ups and extraordinary and unnecessary documentation.

In the early years of the corporation, a car was designed and produced brand new every two years. As the technological advances came into being, it began to take more and more time to accomplish the same outcome. The resultant time could now conceivably take three to four years to accomplish a completed vehicle. When adding the constraints of this timing process, it now took five years. As a result, the participants of the programs were being criticized for things beyond their control, and accomplishing my job became a thorn in the sides of all concerned.

It was a job that I never really enjoyed and one in which I could not achieve the success and admiration that I had accomplished in the past. The Timing Managers who appeared to earn respect were those that hollered loudest and ruled by instilling fear in the recipients of the plan.

The softhearted "yes men" of the old regime were losing ground to the strong and tyrant "yes men" of today. It was always very important that one agree and go along with whatever the corporate movement embodied, and I found myself to be speaking out against those things in which I did not agree.

My frustration mounted to the point that I became short-tempered with a boss who did not return phone calls. I told him that he only had to "press 8" on our automated phone system and say a few words to return my call. This was out of character for me. The corporate gurus who were once admired for their leadership and direction were now leading on a path to destruction. My small voice only drew attention for being disgruntled and not respected.

Before accepting this newly acquired position, I had three choices of jobs from which to choose. Each would have been challenging in its own right, but I was looking for the one that promised me the most advancement in the earliest time frame.

I was now approaching my thirtieth year of employment with the corporation. My reputation had followed me to obtain the position of Program Timing Manager of one of the sporty car lines, the Corvette, which was offered with the promise of attaining the much-clouted eighth-level status within a year of acceptance. I felt that I had earned the right to advance to this next hierarchical level. It didn't happen. Furthermore, this opportunity that seemed to hold the most promise for me turned out to be the biggest mistake I ever made in my corporate life.

It was a difficult and unrewarding assignment. I was put in the position to monitor other's work and progress in meeting time constraints that were made impossible by the corporate-designed and enforced Four Phase Process. The job was called Program Timing, and the people managing each facet of the organization resented the time constraints and my peering over their shoulders to see that their work was accomplished on time.

The engineers, specifically, rightfully regarded the position as preposterous to the real work to be done and sometimes even refused to acknowledge my presence. I was omitted from meeting agendas where I was to make timing presentations and was generally disregarded as having any importance to the organization whatsoever. I was merely tolerated because it was an agreed position that was duplicated within every car line division's organization.

I hadn't been in this capacity too long before I was getting static from one of the engineering groups. It happened to be a female manager who was giving me trouble. My concern grew to the point that I approached my car line manager for help. Mr. Cardine listened to my concerns and advised me to make a particular effort to pacify her. He confided that she had a way of running off at the mouth and that he personally would like to muzzle her. He also told me that I was going to be the one that would have to straighten it out; he couldn't do it for me. She could be difficult, but I would have to work on building a relationship with her.

The next time I approached Mr. Cardine was for a job change. I knew that I could not grow successfully where

I was. I expressed that I had worked in that capacity for a year but felt I would like to return to the manufacturing field. I asked if he had any suggestions for me; he tried to set up a contact for me with an engineering manager, but not for any particular opening.

At the same time, he casually asked me what my long-term plans were with the corporation. I expressed that I hoped to move up to an eighth-level position as, after all, I had been there thirty years now; I felt it was about time.

He seemed to ignore the comment, but I felt it was being stored. I suspected that as soon as I left his office a phone call was made to Don Milton, my homeroom manager. It was not too terribly long before I was promoted. Before I could find a job in manufacturing, I was being rewarded for staying where I was and now would have to stick it out for a period of time. My promotion was announced in a short-notice meeting of the staff and my three current managers of this matrix organization. Mr. Cardine was smiling as he had been a part of this job level change. He was standing at the door, always ready to leave such unimportant meetings.

I would now have the privilege of driving a company car, completely insured, washed, and gassed. This opportunity also should have afforded me other important managerial advantages, such as a mentor, or personal guide, but that was absent. I was left to fend for myself.

Mr. Milton saw to it that I had a car assigned to me immediately. He taught me the ropes in how I was to work with the company car program, and to continue to exchange vehicles after a given number of miles had been driven. I also was to monitor the vehicle's performance and features, and report anything that would not be satisfactory to a customer.

Even though I did not please everyone of the car line staff for which I worked, I still managed to acquire the admiration of these three matrixed bosses. They had obviously agreed that I should be promoted.

In another job, at another time, and in another place, I probably would have succeeded. However, while I now felt I had finally "made it," others sought to destroy me in my newly acquired position.

It was actually right after I received the promotion that the undercurrent of disapproval began to show its face. Another eighth-level manager approached me. He told me that many of the engineering managers were angry about my getting promoted, as they had difficulty in getting their own engineers eighth-level positions. Surely they were more worthy.

I was able to tread water for about the first year. I returned from lunch one day to find the Office Administrator on her hands and knees on my office floor measuring my total floor space. Another eighth-level manager had complained that I had a larger office than he did, and by golly he was right. One of my walls was moved out three inches to accommodate a large printer I needed to do my job. Of course, this was inequitable, and a request was made with the union to move my wall in three inches. It took some time, but it was accomplished to his satisfaction. It was not satisfactory to me, however, as only the front part of the side wall could be moved leaving the wall crooked.

Rearrangement of office space took place regularly, which was a costly expense and a time-wasting event I could never understand. This incident repeated itself when the group again moved to new quarters. My office was again slightly larger than some of the other managers' offices because it happened to fall at the point where a structural pillar stood. The wall was built around the pillar rather than to the inside and again, complaints were heard. I failed to understand the necessity for such pettiness.

While I continued doing the work that I felt was expected of me, background noise of complaints about my work began to erupt. I was doing the best that I could under the circumstances of an unrewarding job. Granted, some others of stronger voice and personality were able to survive their positions much better than I. Being ignored, and not finding anyone to align myself with didn't help matters. The only friend I felt I had was a high-level manager of the group who appeared to befriend me. The noise of complaints had now reached my immediate boss by one of my more vicious counterparts, and a meeting was held about me without my knowledge. I was completely unaware of this meeting and therefore could not even defend myself.

The situation deteriorated until one day my entrusted friend, or so I thought him to be, slipped and verbally referred to my incompetence at a meeting, which was called in an effort to support me. All of his back peddling could not erase the sting or embarrassment to me or to the speaker of the comment. The damage was now done. Obviously, similar words had been openly discussed behind my back previously in the meeting held without my knowledge. Two hours of apology in a private meeting after work between the speaker and myself did not correct the harm done.

Other incidents followed where I found I had been left off of meeting notices or situations where I attended meetings but was kept from contributing. At one meeting my verbal contribution was actually refused, and I then left the meeting angry and defeated. There was obviously no point in my being there.

A new Program Manager replaced my current boss and called a meeting to introduce himself to the Business Team, of which I was a member. Mr. Duffy was a stuffed-shirt businessman who sought to impress upon the group that he was approachable, down-to-earth, and a family man. He didn't fully convince me.

During this meeting, he spoke from notes taken at a previous meeting that he had attended. He asked for the appropriate persons of this group to take the assignments of the work that needed to be done. Assignments followed until everyone in the room had accepted one or more pieces of work except me. The meeting was over and everyone was dismissed. I felt remiss in not having an assignment in hand upon leaving his office, so I stayed after to introduce myself and explain to him the work that I did.

During the meeting he had been slightly flirtatious with me, with an approving glance or facial expression. I let that pass, and proceeded to approach the matter professionally. He appreciated my efforts and work explanation, and that was the last time I actually spoke to the man.

Soon my homeroom boss saw to it that I was to switch positions with another person in the group holding a lower position on another car program. She was to take my managerial position, and I was to do her job at my existing level. The person I was to report to was of the same level as myself, but one who had the gift of a commanding personality. She was definitely the right person for the job, and I was certain that she would succeed to a higher level of management. We worked with this arrangement for another year, with me trying to get out of this predicament gracefully and obtain another position where I could succeed and go on.

As happens in large corporations, I was blackballed from most other positions, and sought to enlist the services of a newly assigned manager to our department. He was an aristocratic type, and after a couple of appeals to him in private meetings, he agreed to assist me. I made lists of opportunities where I felt I could succeed. He made suggestions as well, and I naively thought that I was going to get his help and out of this situation.

When he became the group leader of my department, he called a meeting to introduce himself. He announced himself as Howard Thiesen. I immediately recognized him as someone I had dealt with before. He went on to explain his background and stated the name of the plant where he had been a Planning Manager prior to coming to Michigan. I had been a Program Coordinator in a manufacturing capacity where I monitored programs at assembly plants. I had made his acquaintance during that time. I tried to break the steel barrier of his demeanor by relating to our previous work encounter. I received no smile or acknowledgement. He was perturbed that I should know him at all and used this stature to strengthen his position.

The meeting went something like this:

> HOWARD THIESEN III
> Good Morning. I'm Howard Thiesen, and I'm the new Group Manager replacing Mr. Worthington. I'll be having a staff meeting with you every Monday morning in this conference room. I've had Julia reserve this room for the remainder of this year.

There were murmurs of acceptance and welcome from the group.

> HOWARD THIESEN III
> I graduated from LaSalle University, School of Engineering. I also attended General Motors Institute. As some of you may know, I come from a long background of Quality jobs; I came up through the ranks at the Ternstedt Division, and I served as Planning Administrator for the Fairfax, Kansas City Assembly Plant. I'll be here to assist you, so if you need to talk to me, just make an appointment with Julia. My schedule gets pretty busy, but I'll be sure to meet with you.

Now, let's hear about some of your backgrounds.

He looked toward Linda O'Claire for her to proceed. Linda was a well-adjusted, outspoken young gal, whose opinions were sometimes admittedly found to be obnoxious. I was now reporting to her.

> LINDA O'CLAIRE
> Hi.   I'm Linda O'Claire, and I'm Planning Manager for the C Car Platform. I graduated from Mumford U, also in Engineering, and came to General Motors right after graduation. I've been here a few years myself, and most recently in the Parts Expediting Department.   I've been in this department for the last three years.

Howard Thiesen looked down the table to the next person.

> HOWARD THIESEN III
> How about you, Ken?

Ken Centurion was a junior member of the group, very quiet and a tecky-type. He had spent all of his time working with data and computers.

> KEN CENTURION
> Sure.   I'm Ken Centurion, and I'm Planning Manager for the A and L Platform. I graduated from Illinois State and I worked as a contract employee for

the first two years after graduation. I
now work directly for General Motors.

Howard Thiesen III again looked down the table to the
next person.

HOWARD THIESEN III
And how about you?

ELLEN
Hi. I'm Ellen Blend, and I'm Sub-
Systems Manager for the C Car under
Linda. I graduated with a Masters
Degree from Central Michigan
University, and I also took classes at
General Motors Institute.

I then smiled at Howard Thiesen and said:

ELLEN
I think we've met before. I used to be
Program Planning Coordinator for
Production Engineering, and I traveled
to many of the plants to monitor
programs. I think you were Planning
Administrator at Fairfax when I was
there.

HOWARD THIESEN III
Maybe. I don't remember seeing you.
How about you, uh, . . . and directed his
attention to the next person at the table.

Marcie Moran was an overly energetic gal, both cute and
refined, with exceptional capability. She was a recent

victim of the corporation's poor management and lost an entry-level managerial position to one of the other men in the group, Clayton O'Connor.

> MARCIE MORAN
> Hi. I'm Marcie Moran, and I work for
> Ken as a Sub-Systems Timing Manager.
> I worked for Parts Engineering before
> coming to this department.

Howard Thiesen continued to address the next person at the table.

> HOWARD THIESEN III
> And your name?

Carolyn Bartell was a charming and attractive enigmatic gal with a bouncy personality. She beamed from ear to ear and made a notable impression.

> CAROLYN BARTELL
> I'm Carolyn Bartell and I'm Planning
> Manager for the D Platform. I used to
> work in Warranty.

Howard Thiesen now addressed Clayton with a glance.

Clayton O'Connor was an incompetent man who had made it up through the ranks by chance and the 'good-old-boys network.' He was now an eighth-level manager. His personality was impudent and negative. His expression was one of a cat who had just swallowed a canary.

CLAYTON O'CONNOR
I'm Clayton O'Connor, and I'm
Program Manager of A and C Platforms.
Carol Ashton (looking to his right) here,
works for me and does the sub-systems
timing.

Carol Ashton was afraid of her own shadow. She did
her job out of fear and generally felt persecuted.

HOWARD THIESEN III
And you, Carol, what is your
background previous to this department?

CAROL ASHTON
Carol answered meekly, "I used to work
in Purchasing."

HOWARD THIESEN III
And how long have you been here?

CAROL ASHTON
About a year now.

Glancing toward the last person at the table.

HOWARD THIESEN III
And lastly, . . .

Joe Welton was an accomplished man for the level he
had achieved. He was friendly, accommodating, and
personable. He stated his position.

Picking up his book, Howard Thiesen gave his closing comments.

> HOWARD THIESEN III
> Very well. It was nice meeting all of
> you today. I'll see you all next Monday,
> same time, in this room.

The group then shuffled out into the hallway to return to their respective offices.

After my second appeal to Howard Thiesen for a managerial position in his newly formed staff, he refused; then he shared a very important piece of information with me. He showed me a copious letter that had been placed in my file and passed along to him. It had been artfully written by none other than Scott Warner, the man who I thought was my entrusted friend. Scott Warner was also the one who slipped with the comment of my incompetence and who had apologized prophetically. I never would have guessed that this man would be two-faced and agree to write such a devastating and destructive letter about me which led to my assured demise.

By then Scott Warner had left the corporation, a move that almost never took place in the earlier years of my employment with the corporation. He was now out of state and was a Vice President of another firm.

I asked Mr. Thiesen if I could make a copy of the letter, to which he agreed, but I was to return it to him immediately. He also stated that because of it, he was unable to place me in a managerial position. It would also be very difficult for me to clear my name in order to move on.

My gentleman friend, Matt, was a nice-looking, tall and fair-complected hunk with thinning hair. We discussed how I was being victimized much like he had been while he was employed with General Motors.

Matt had twenty-three years in with the company when he was pigeon-holed into a job that was unfitting. He was monitored daily on a P.I.P., Performance Improvement Program, which only made matters worse.

As he said, "Once they get on your trail, you can't shake them, and you don't even know what you did wrong." Consequently, he was fired for insubordination, but he never did find out why he was really fired.

I, of course, confronted the perpetrator of this horrible letter in writing referring to this correspondence as having been authored by my entrusted friend.

It was several weeks before I received a written response. He stated that the delay was due to his being totally enraged at the circumstances in which he had been placed and consequently found. He did not mention his remorse of having written the letter or of it being shared with me. He was more concerned with how this letter would ultimately affect him since he had been responsible for the displacement of many personnel as well as myself. He stated that he asked the question of Mr. Weaver of Personnel, who handled his departure, if the corporation would defend him if he were to be embroiled in a lawsuit as a result of any of his directed actions. He was angered that Mr. Weaver only laughed and told him that he would be totally on his own; he would have no recourse.

No interviews were made available to me through Mr. Thiesen except one, which I particularly remember. All other contacts resulted in telephone conversations with jobs not materializing. This interview was by personal arrangement by Mr. Thiesen and was perfunctory, at best. When I called back to inquire as to the status of the selection process, it became blatantly obvious to me that I had been set up to feel that I had had a real interview.

The interview was one in which I could have filled many of the open slots in a newly forming organization. I was disqualified over an issue of travel by their stating that I found travel to be objectionable. This was not the case. The plan was to see that I failed, and this new boss now requested that I come and work directly for him. In that way I would be placed in a visible position to prove my worth, and in time I would be able to move on to better things. I almost did. There may have been some sincerity at the base of this action; however, it did not work out to my advantage.

This new position required that I work with another eighth-level manager who somehow had accomplished obtaining a contracted three-day-a-week job. Karen was a young, bright gal who had graduated from one of the much-acclaimed schools like Purdue, and was easily living up to its reputation. She was truly a scholar, grasped things quickly, and was able to organize and spew out intelligible information in a timely manner.

My requests to meet with the boss were minimally satisfied and generally treated as nuisance interruptions to his day. Getting clear direction from this man was difficult, but Karen had the ability to break into his heavy schedule for one-on-one meetings on the days that she worked. I was treated as a lowly employee who was to take the information that Karen obtained and "hang it on the wall" in a locked conference room for the viewing by other managers. It was a process called "Visual Management."

The information contained financial data, as well as the current key processes of the corporation such as "lean engineering" and "lean manufacturing." This activity might include my creating some graphical presentation which Karen felt apologetically unequipped to do, and to be a Corporate Paper Hanger.

Whoever thought to subscribe to the teachings of Visual Management while yet endorsing corporate security? Where was the logic? It is incredibly laughable to me to begin to describe the almost countless person hours that continue to be spent in "hanging useless paper on the walls" to show engineering processes and configurations that were once contained in files and binders. Why not take out an ad in the Wall Street Journal so that everyone could more easily view the corporate secrets?

Sure, rooms were locked upon leaving, paper was taped over all glass windows, and keys were held by a select few in order to protect this precious information. Why hide this information when most employees in the meeting rooms and offices were not real employees anyway? Most were on contractual assignments and had little to no loyalty to the corporation. Furthermore, most engineering designs were and still are located offsite at engineering houses that are frequented by employees of all other automobile companies. This leaves few secrets anyway. And what about the cleaning crew?

It is probably no wonder why, during the demise of my proud and acquired position to eighth-level manager, that I began to retaliate. I was asked what I thought of the new and probably highly paid, consultant-designed process of taping folders to the outside walls of meeting rooms. These folders were to contain an accurate accounting of each and every engineering change to parts or assemblies along their various stages of development.

Can you imagine the costs involved in person hours, paper, and effort to keep these folders updated daily? Their purpose was for some unknowing manager to just pick out the contents of each folder for review at any given time to learn of its status. So why couldn't any passer-by in the hallways also learn whatever was in the contents of these unsecured folders?

Surely any good manager would not be lurking the hallways peering through folders on walls to obtain the status of his program. He would be on top of each facet of his program's development daily by meeting with his team. Obviously, I retorted by saying, "It's another piece of corporate stupidity." You can see how my popularity soon waned.

The actions of the corporation were no longer making any sense to me at all. It was time to get out. The little gerbils in their habitrails were just following one another munching on the shredded paper of the Visual

Management and wall folder systems.   We needed
leaders.   Automobile companies bred followers, and
what we had was a lot of people following each other
around. Thus, I wrote the following editorial.

Editorial

Failing Companies Failing Their People

After years of prosperous fortune and challenging experiences, many companies are finding themselves in a state of decline. Doing business the same way, ever perfecting their methods, profits are diminishing if not becoming extinct. Research and development no longer hold the same importance.

Profit sharing, once a company perk, for some companies is nonexistent. Bonuses have reached similar status. Employee contributions in the workplace, like paying for the morning coffee and donuts in meetings, buying your own daily planner to be used on the job, and bringing in your own software, are on the rise. Companies just don't have the money to spend.

While all companies wavered on an annual seesaw of spend vs. austerity when it was time to make budgets meet forecasts, many companies today know only of cost cutting meetings and programs. Everything unnecessary to run a business is being eliminated at the cost of morale.

Still holding people as a company's most important asset, people aren't being made to feel important. And more often than not, lip service is only paid as a maxim, while plans are being made to cut those not thought to provide strength to the company in lean times. "Bottom feeders," I once heard in a company meeting, referring to those employees who weren't top producers; "I can only carry so many on my payroll."

This barks the questions: Has the company trained its workforce properly? Have they assisted their people to advance in the organization? Have they been careful to not overlook even the first-line employees who also take pride in their workmanship? I think not.

People need positive reinforcement. They need to know when they have done a good job and be directed toward challenge and advancement whenever possible. They must have confidence bestowed upon them and be given a "halo" effect in the eyes of their supervision. When was the last time you got or gave a real "attaboy"? That's what makes top performers.

When employees reach saturation on their jobs and need to grow, they don't need to hear "You don't have the experience," or "You're not qualified," or "You don't have the background." That's what stifles an organization and makes poor producers. Lack of incentive or fulfillment of promise; no recognition, monetary or verbal; absence of opportunity, self-enrichment, self-enlightenment--these are the missing attributes of failing companies who fail their people.

Chapter Seven

The Resultant Factor

I was called in by Mr. Thiesen to learn that I would be taking another eighth-level position that was of suitable responsibility and to my liking. I would become the Core Timing Manager and be responsible for the output of the other Timing Managers. It would be one in which I could redeem myself after such bereavement, and I would assume this position on November 1 of that year, 1993. I was pleased that my paper hanging days would soon be over.

Then, an attack was made upon Karen, my talented co-worker, by none other than Howard Thiesen III. He demanded that she work five days per week instead of three in a matter of a couple of weeks, or else be terminated. It was stated that because I was leaving, she was needed full time.

She argued that she held that position by written contract. He eluded to the fact that her limited hours worked did not meet his requirements and that Personnel would not uphold her written agreement. She replied that she did not wish to work five days per week. She had two small children at home, and that is why she had applied for the contracted position. She also stated that she did not care if she spent her time pulling staples, as long as she only worked three days per week.

Meetings took place between her and members of Personnel and their inherent committees, and an agreement was made in order to satisfy the requirements of Mr. Thiesen. Karen would have to find a position of her own seeking within the two-week time frame, or else be out of a job. Should she be successful, she could be transferred and live out the duration of her contract. How the "good old boys network" reigned in that corporation!

I was taking a week's vacation with my friend, Gwenn, prior to taking on my new position. As a prudent employee, I checked my voice mail mid-week while on vacation. I retrieved a message from the secretary regarding an 8 o'clock meeting that had been scheduled with Mr. Thiesen on the first day of my return. Of course, I responded that I would be there, and appropriately asked for the subject of the meeting. I received no response. No response meant big trouble.

When I arrived at the office for the meeting the following Monday, I found that Diane Hillsdale from Personnel was also to be in this meeting. That naturally meant big, big trouble. Fortunately, my friend Gwenn and I had rehearsed every possibility in order to be well prepared for whatever was to follow. Gwenn had some Personnel work experience herself. Getting fired was quite remote as I had put in so many good years with the corporation; however, I found that logic does not always prevail in such matters.

Howard Thiesen III spoke. "You will not be taking on the new position as originally discussed." Now, slightly stammering, "You will be taking on some of the duties of that position, but you won't be taking that job. I don't feel that you are doing the work of an eighth-level manager."

I could see that keeping my eighth-level position had now been threatened, and I was enraged at the comment that I was not doing eighth-level work. I had, afterall, been assigned to hang paper on the wall! *Of course I understood* that was not eighth-level work.

"Excuse me," I said, "but you assigned me to hang paper on the wall!"

He acted as though I should not feel impoverished to take on such a lowly responsibility, as even unclassified managers hung paper on the wall as part of their jobs!

"Part of their jobs" was a key point. It was not their entire job.

"You will take this job as a seventh level," he continued.

I replied, "You have no documentation to do this."

"What do you mean, I have no documentation. What kind of documentation?"

"You have no documentation," I repeated.

Again, "What kind of documentation?" he was still asking.

As mundane and monotone as I could be, I continued to repeat this rhetoric. "You have no documentation."

This few-worded conversation went on for several minutes, with Diane Hillsdale from Personnel sitting there as witness.

Finally, it was agreed that there was nothing more to say; I alluded to the fact that legally I had my rights, and that he did not have the required documentation to demote me from my position. He certainly had no grounds to retract an offer made so recently.

Upon leaving the meeting, Diane privately added that I was not the only person who was to receive this action. It did not comfort me, but I was curious as to what she meant.

Later that day I called my previous boss, Don Milton, who was most responsible for my promotion to eighth level.

"I just had something shocking happen," I said. "Remember me telling you that I was getting the Timing Core Position?"

"Yes," said Don Milton.

"Well, it was just retracted," I exclaimed.

"Are you kidding?" he asked.

"No, I'm not. And they're putting me under John Nelson as a seventh-level manager," I stated.

"Very interesting. I've got a similar situation here with Kevin Bender," Mr. Milton went on to say. "In Kevin's case, I asked if they wanted him demoted, and they said no. They just want him gone!"

"So what are you going to do?" I asked.

"I'm trying to get him transferred to Saturn."

"Oh, my!"

"I'm sorry to hear what's happening to you. If I hear anything, I'll let you know. Keep me posted," said Mr. Milton.

Karen was able to find an appropriate position and was able to stay on with her three-day a week job. I was pleased for her.

Chapter Eight

My Search for an Attorney

On November 1, I took over the new, lowly position, with the sole responsibility of keeping an ever-changing distribution list of timing schedule recipients up to date. On December 1, five other eighth-level managers in the Quality Department were demoted.

At someone's suggestion, I immediately requested a second phone line be installed to take messages for the distribution list. If I had answered every call, I would have done nothing else, and it would have driven me mad. How it got approved and installed is beyond me, but others still thought that I was an eighth level and marched to my orders. As time went on, I became chief of the fire brigade, safety committee, phone system installations, computer upgrades and office moves.

I also began to take days off when necessary to look for an attorney and file a complaint with E.E.O.C. at Gwenn's recommendation. I did not turn in my company car. Frankly, they forgot to tell me to, and since no one asked for it I continued to drive it. I even drove to E.E.O.C. and ignored the parking ticket I received as it wasn't my personal vehicle that was parked there. In the end I had to pay it, but I made them work real hard for the money.

When I first arrived in the new department, I met with my boss, John Nelson. He was very sympathetic to my situation and confided in me that he did not agree with the corporation's actions. If there was anything he could do to make my circumstances more tolerable, he would be glad to do it.

My concern was to find a good lawyer. I went to Mr. Thiesen's secretary's desk, while both he and she were away, and ripped out the entire section of attorneys from the telephone book.

I called several firms and met with a few. At this time, I didn't even know what I was suing for. I just knew that I had been very wronged.

One evening, when Matt came over, he told me that he had crossed paths with a man that we had worked with at General Motors. That man claimed that he had sued General Motors for his job loss and that he won his case. Matt found out who his attorney was and suggested that I call him.

This attorney told me that Leon's case was very unusual. He basically said the man was a mental case and needed someone to fight for him; my circumstances were entirely different, and he didn't think he could help. I felt that he didn't think that he could fight General Motors successfully.

I then received a telephone call from Personnel asking me if I had driven a particular car and received a ticket while parking downtown. The car I had been driving was not actually assigned to me, but one that I had traded with another driver of company cars. So, I said no, that I had not been assigned such a car.

By the next week, Mr. Nelson stepped inside my office to deliver a message. "They want your car turned in within two weeks," John Nelson said.

"I don't have anything else to drive," I stated.

"Well, they feel two weeks is enough time for you to get another car."

I argued that it takes longer than that to get a car through the company car-buying program. He said if that's what I intended to do, he would see if they would work with me on that.

I thanked him, but had absolutely no intention of paying a minimum of $18,000 to the corporation for a new car of my liking. I just wasn't going to do it.

In the meantime, I looked for used cars. I was pretty particular in finding one that had not been smoked in since smoke bothered my lungs immensely.

One day I went to a used-car lot on my lunch hour. I looked over used cars noting paint chips, dented fenders, and one with a crack in the rear fascia. I spoke to the used car salesman asking if they didn't have anything clean that hadn't been smoked in. I was already annoyed that I had to do this at all.

They tried to accommodate me by pulling a car around that had just been cleaned up. I took one look at the interior of the car and saw that the carpeting was all matted from just having been shampooed. It looked terribly used. I told the salesman that this wouldn't do either, thanked him, and left discouraged.

My friend, Matt, also shopped for cars for me, but found nothing he felt suitable for me to drive. He kept checking with me to see if I had found one, but I'm sure that memories from his past situation with the corporation weighed heavily upon him.

After he was fired, I sent him to an attorney that I found listed in the yellow pages. He liked him very much but was afraid to sue. He felt that he might find it difficult to find employment elsewhere if it were at all traceable on his record. He ended up just living with the hatred.

My friend, Gwenn, called me to say that she had just heard about someone who had a case similar to mine, and the law firm was Crumpet and Sax. "They're in downtown Detroit," she said. "I think you should send them a cover letter and some facts about your case. See if they'll take it."

I agreed that I would get it ready that evening.

Gwenn also asked, "By the way, have they told you why you were demoted yet?"

"No, not really," I said.

"Then write a letter to Mr. Thiesen and ask him," she directed.

"Ask him in writing?" I said.

"Yes. That's exactly what you need to do."

"Okay, I will." I always did as she said, as she was always right.

My letter said, "Dear Mr. Thieson: Please provide in writing reasons for my demotion on November 1, 1993."

I saved the letter on a disc at home as I had been saving all other information pertinent to my situation.

A week or so later, the telephone rang at my office; it was the law firm that had been recommended by Gwenn. Beverly Musset's comments were short and abrupt.

"I've just read your case. It's very interesting, but I can't take it," she hastened.

I imagined her to be an early-forties woman with short, neat hair, and finely dressed in a tailored suit.

"Oh?" I answered in partial shock.

"I'm a corporate attorney. I work for the corporate side, so I can't represent the employee."

"Oh, I see." I understood her reasoning.

"I can recommend someone for you, however," she offered.

"That would be great. Who do you recommend?" I asked.

"She's actually a friend of mine. Her name is Sarah Bertel. She's with Sampson and Torey. They're downtown, too."

"Okay," I said slowly.

Beverly provided the address and telephone number.

Harry Rogue, an admiring male counterpart, entered my office as I hung up the phone. We engaged in general chitchat, and I welcomed his interruption to my strained thoughts. Harry was dark-haired, round-faced, and a rather large, well-built man in his early-fifties. He was a sweetheart and no doubt interested in a personal relationship, but definitely not my type. I enjoyed him as a friend.

"Here, I brought you some totally fat-free cookies that my daughter made last night," Harry offered.

"Oh, thanks, Harry. That's really nice of you," I said.

"She's really into this health thing for me since my heart attack, you know."

Harry had been one of several to follow that had suffered a heart attack due to ill treatment or just plain job stress.

"I probably need to watch the fat in my diet, too," I offered.

"Yes. Everyone should. You should drink skimmed milk, too," he added.

When I got home from work one evening and looked over my mail, I curiously looked at the envelope from Sampson and Torey. Its contents read:

Dear Ms. Blend:

I reviewed the documentation which you forwarded to this office.

Please be advised that I do not believe we would be successful in pursuing this action on your behalf. However, that does not mean you do not have a cause of action.

If you wish to pursue this matter, you must do so within three years from the date of the illegal discrimination or you will be forever barred from pursuing the cause of action.

I am returning to you copies of the documents which you forwarded to me. Thank you for considering our office. I am sorry we are unable to assist you.

I called Gwenn with this information.

"Don't take it personally," she said. "Maybe they feel there's not enough money in it for them. They're probably too big and you're too small for them to take on as a client."

I was quite discouraged.

"You know, I took that Dale Carnegie class not too long ago; one of the fellows in the class had been in law enforcement and now is an attorney. I think he deals with discrimination," I said.

"Give him a call. What's he like?" asked Gwenn.

"He's kind of quiet, but very sensitive and caring from what I can tell. He reminds me of your friend, Cal," I said. Cal was a police officer who preferred teaching safety to kids rather than working the beat.

"Well, go see him. You won't really know until you meet with him," she offered.

"By the way, have you received an answer to your letter yet?" she asked.

"No, I haven't," I admitted.

"You probably won't, either. They don't have anything they can put in writing. You should get a copy of your personnel file though. They have to give it to you by law," she instructed.

"Okay. I'll ask for it," I said.

"And about that letter asking about your demotion?" she continued.

"Yes?" I asked.

"This time write to Personnel."

The next day there was a message on my work voice mail.

"This is Howard Thiesen. I am going on vacation and that car is to be turned in. You can respond to me of your intentions through voice mail or let John Nelson know."

I sighed heavily and thought to myself, *that coward doesn't have the courage to face me in person or to ask me to come to his office.* I decided . . . saying softly to myself,

"If called by a panther, don't anther!"[*]

While sitting on my couch at home one evening, Matt and I talked about my situation. He recalled my having sent him to an attorney that he liked. This time Matt referred him back to me. He said that he felt that I would like the man and that I should at least go and talk to him.

I met with Bud Wiseman one evening right after work. Matt was right; I liked him very much. He was very disarming, had a vivacious personality, and his feet were firmly planted in his work. Unlike other attorneys I had met with, this man was not pompous. He didn't find it necessary to impress upon me how wonderful he was. Instead, he told me how he really liked his work and his job. He found it both fun and rewarding.

After some discussion, I asked, "So what do you think?"

"You definitely have a case," he said.

Again, somewhat confused what this wrongful action should be called, "What would I be suing for?" I asked.

---

[*] Poet, Ogden Nash, (1902-1971)

63

"Age discrimination, and maybe sexual discrimination, too. We'll have to look at all the details," he commented.

"Fine," I said. "How about if I send you the log I've been keeping?" I offered.

"You've been keeping a log?" he asked surprisingly.

"Yes," I said. "Every time something notable happens within the corporation regarding my situation or other people, I document it."

"That's wonderful. Yes, send it to me and we'll get back together again," he said.

I talked to Gwenn on the telephone and she asked if I had received anything from Personnel about my demotion yet. I told her that I had not.

"It's time to write them another letter," she said.

This time I said, "They not only haven't told me why I was demoted, they haven't told me what my position is. I don't know if I'm an entry-level sweeper or a seventh-level whatever. I also don't know what my pay range is," I said.

"Well, that's what you need to ask them. Put it in writing. Documentation, remember?" she reminded me.

"I sure do," I stated.

She then asked if I had received my personnel file yet. I told her that I had received a call just that day and was told I could have a copy, but that it would cost me ten cents a page. They suggested since it was so large that I might not want to do that.

She hoped that I had told them that I wanted it all, and I did. I could pick it up later that week.

Chapter Nine

Groundwork

I was still procrastinating on turning in the company car. One day John Nelson, still doing Howard Thiesen's dirty work for him, stood just outside my office door. He said, "I had a call from Alex White of Personnel. He tells me that General Motors is under audit, and if the car is not turned in by Monday it will be reported as stolen."

"Stolen!" I said. Then I caught on to the ploy. I regained my composure, smiled and said, "They know where it is!"

I was shaken, but smiled and walked away.

The telephone rang, and it was Personnel informing me that I could pick up my file. It would cost me $8.00.

When I went to pick up the file, I was shocked at its small size. I had seen it quite recently and it was now about half the size. When I asked what happened, I was told that it had just been cleaned up of duplicate material.

When I told this to Gwenn, she was satisfied and said that whatever was in there was all that they could enter into court.

"Are your appraisals in it?" she asked.

"Every one," I said. "And there is not one that has a rating less than highly effective."

"So they're all okay," she verified.

"Sure. They're fine. And all of the records of my raises are in there too."

"Is there a copy of your demotion in there?"

I laughed. "No, there isn't."

"Well I guess they haven't officially demoted you then, have they!"

Gwenn then cautioned me. "You're not talking to anyone at work about your situation, are you?"

I told her that I wasn't, but that some people were really trying to help me out. They were offering to bring me information, and every week I would get a call about someone being mistreated or others of a similar situation who did not receive the same treatment as I did.

She agreed that was very nice, but warned me again. "Don't trust anyone. Be very careful. They are going to send someone to you posing as a friend, but they are really looking for information. You will have a hard time telling who this person is, because they will be carefully selected. It will be someone you least expect."

I took her warning very seriously. She knew what she was talking about. "Be nice to everyone," she said, "but refuse to talk about your situation."

I agreed that I would.

Matt came over and suggested that we go out for a very nice dinner and some wine that evening. I thought that would be a very good idea after all of the stress that I had been dealing with. He was always saying, "I think we should do something nice this evening." We both enjoyed dressing up to go out, and I appreciated his generous and kind nature.

In time, things became palatable in this new job assignment. John Nelson actually gave me a special project to do that earned me some respect. I was placed in charge of the timing aspect of the varying glove box contents that would be going into the vehicles from all car divisions. I did a marvelous job. The car divisions loved me. The man who ran the committee loved me.

Just before I was to see the project to completion, John Nelson pulled me off of the job. He said that he would take over from there so that I could be placed on another project. I wasn't going to be allowed to bask in the glory of a job well done. That, too, was taken from me. The group that I had been working for screamed and hollered for my return. They called John Nelson and requested that I be allowed to finish the assignment. They gave me great praise, which I appreciated, but could do nothing about.

I was in a one-on-one meeting with John Nelson, and I asked him if there was a chance that I could get my eighth level back since I had done such a good job. He told me that he could not do that for me, but suggested that I work hard at my current assignment. I told him that I always did, but that it wasn't gratifying if I couldn't be rewarded.

His parting words were that he couldn't promote me, but that I had to have a plan. I responded, leaving his office with, "Oh, I have a plan!"

John Nelson told me that he would pass the information on to Howard Thiesen to let him know that I had done a good job. It was no doubt Thiesen's direction that I be pulled off of the job before completion anyway. John Nelson did not attend to my job in my absence as he said he would do. He never could find the time.

Carolyn Bartell stopped by my office to ask if I was going to Mr. Thiesen's staff meeting that day. I told her that I was.

She then asked if I had heard that Ken Centurion had been promoted to the Timing Core position. I had not known this, so I asked her if they were announcing it at the meeting.

She said that they were, and she thought that I had better know before walking in there. I thanked her kindly and immediately called Marcie Moran to let her know. Marcie was working for Ken Centurion and probably didn't know either.

I was right. Marcie didn't know.

"They sure do take care of the men, don't they?" she said.

"Yes, they do," I had to agree.

They had actually waited six months to fill the position after they took it from me. They probably figured I wasn't going to sue since so much time had elapsed.

Marcie continued, "He's not even a leader. I work for him and he doesn't even talk to me. I have to force him to say good morning."

"I know," I said. "I just thought I'd let you know since he's your boss."

"Thanks. After all you and I have been through here, and they still pull this stuff," she commented.

Marcie had a Timing Manager position as did I for another car line. Her car line had many more vehicles than mine did and she needed assistance. Instead of giving her the help that she required, they pulled her off of the job, replaced her with Clayton O'Connor, promoted him, and gave him an assistant.

I gallantly entered Howard Thiesen's conference room and sat directly across from him at the head of the table. I proceeded to look right into his face.

"Good morning, Mr. Thiesen," I said.

Howard Thiesen responded coolly, "Good morning."

Carolyn Bartell sat toward the back of the room and smiled at me for my courage and boldness. I returned a smirk that went into a smile.

Howard Thiesen began. "We have a couple of new assignments here in the group that I'd like to announce. Ken Centurion will be the new Timing Core Manager."

The group applauded lightly.

"And Margaret Roman, new to our group, will manage the new Financial Parts Tracking System. Please welcome her to our group."

This was to be my new assignment, working in the parts tracking group for Margaret Roman. I would again be reporting to another eighth-level female manager. This gal was wholesome, self assured and a very hard worker. She corralled her group of grunts together regularly to talk over the job and to command the work to be done. Reluctantly, I stooped to her direction. The computer system we had to work with was, in my opinion, a real joke. The programming was new and unperfected. It did not perform correctly for many months to come, if ever. It was a loathsome job.

My wonderful assignment was to verify reams of computer-generated runoffs of financial part cost information. I was to gather the information weekly from various teams, input the data and verify the reports. I hated it. Looking at numbers with a fine-toothed comb did not appeal to me.

We were all in agreement that much work was needed to make the system work correctly. We all witnessed that numbers would be entered into the system, and the next time the data was pulled up on the screen the numbers had all changed. I was wasting my time verifying numbers that would never be right.

Margaret Roman cracked the whip each time that I saw her. She insisted that I work faster and get the reports out more frequently. It was an impossible situation. She criticized me one too many times, and I let her know it.

"Margaret," I said, "I'm getting really tired of your criticism of me. Really tired." And I got up and walked out of her office. It was reported to John Nelson immediately.

I still did not have a response from my letters to Personnel. So early in the morning, before most arrived at work, I again slipped a letter and copies under the locked doorways of the Personnel offices. I then scurried back to my office.

Later that morning, I was visited by two members of the Personnel staff. Alex White was accompanied by Diane Hillsdale who lagged slightly behind him at my office door. Diane really didn't want to be a part of this, but it was her job.

"You have to turn in the keys to your car by the end of the day," Alex stated.

"That's fine," I coolly stated. "Just tell me why Allen Sheppard left the company and is still driving a company car." I had been given good ammunition.

"I don't know that he's still driving one of our cars," Alex said.

"Well, he is. And he still has a phone line here, too."

Now I had him.

"Well, that has nothing to do with you," he blustered. "You still have to turn in the keys."

"Sure," I said. "Just as soon as you state in writing reasons why I am being treated differently, and I will."

Alex White was red-faced and raised his voice at me. "I'll do no such thing! When you lose your level, you lose your car! Just bring those keys to my office by the end of the day."

I was obviously shaken, but literally smiled at my accomplishment. I arranged for a ride to the doctor's office and home that evening. At the end of the day, I cleared everything off of my desk and left the company car keys in my desk drawer.

When I got home, I briefly looked at my mail, placed it on the kitchen counter, leaving it unopened. I was emotionally drained and went directly to bed. I awakened later on.

My daughter, Sue, was home all evening. She was about twenty-five, a pretty girl of small-to-medium build, and quite concerned about me. She told me that my boss had called and she had told him that I was sleeping. He had asked that I call him at home later and gave her his home telephone number.

I told her that I would leave him a message on his work voice mail later.

I sat on the couch and proceeded to watch some television, thinking about what I would say when I called John Nelson. Later that evening, I checked my voice mail messages to find that John Nelson had left me a message there as well, and Alex White of Personnel had left two, all regarding the car. John Nelson's message was as follows:

"I got a call from Personnel, and they want to see if something can't be worked out on the car. I need to know the facts on whether or not you ordered a car and if you did, when it will be in. They thought that maybe they could expedite the order. Also, Howard Thiesen said that he thought a meeting between he, Alex White, you and I would be in order."

I composed my thoughts and left a message for John Nelson. I had been warned by Gwenn to never get into a meeting that was two or more against one, namely me!

> Hi, John. I'm calling from home. After the scene that took place in my office today, I went to the doctor and he told me that I should stay home for three weeks. The car keys are in my desk drawer. I also picked up two messages from Alex White this evening asking me to call him. He wanted to see if we couldn't work something out on the car, but I don't know if I will call him. I also received your message about the car and the request for a meeting, but I

am not up for conversation, nor am I up
for a three- or four-way meeting.

Later that evening, I opened my mail. There was a copy
of a letter from Civil Rights (E.E.O.C.) to General
Motors.

No wonder they wanted to cooperate on the car now!

The next morning there was a knock on the door. It was
my son, Doug. He had arranged to drop off his car to
me and said that I could keep it for as long as I needed.
I'm sure that Sue had tipped him off on what had been
happening.

He said that he had arranged for transportation and really
didn't need a car. I told him that I would probably not
be off of work for very long.

It was now January of 1994, and I was to have my
second meeting with Bud Wiseman. He had reviewed
all of my information and said that it looked great.

"Did you get that article that I sent you on the *Glass
Ceiling*?" he asked.

I said "Yes," that I did.

"I really believe that's a big problem for women. They
can only get so high in a corporation, and then they
reach a glass ceiling. They can't see it, but it's there.
They aren't allowed to get any higher."

"I don't know if it applies to me," I said thoughtfully.

"No? Well, maybe you don't see it, but it may be there," he debated.

When we met again, I asked about how he felt the chances were to sue such a large corporation. He said that they were no different than anyone else. Some attorneys that I spoke with wouldn't take the case. He didn't seem to be threatened by them.

I then asked, "What do you think the case is worth?" It seemed to be an appropriate question to ask.

"It's really hard to say," he said. "I could give you a range, but I'll know more as the case develops. I have to tell you, there is no set amount for any case. It can change dramatically as the case unfolds, or by what is hot at the time."

"Well, it's not about money anyway," I said.

"It's always about money!" he said.

"No . . . it isn't," I insisted. "It's about principle!"

We then proceeded to start documenting the details. As the case progressed, at his suggestion, I continued to send copies of my documented pages as new incidents occurred. I didn't know it then, but it was a marvelous story in the making.

Chapter Ten

You Can't Retire

I began to twitch at work. It started out to be a few times each morning and then again in the afternoon. The twitches became so frequent that I began charting them on a notepad at my desk. The tick marks were filling the page. I didn't know what was happening to me. They numbered up to 60 spasms per day. I knew I had to get help.

I made an appointment with the doctor. He put me on some anti-anxiety drug that I hated. I didn't like feeling drugged, and I couldn't work with them. He changed the prescription a few times before I found one that I could tolerate. I didn't like being medicated and I still twitched.

I asked to see John Nelson after one of our staff meetings one morning. We met later that day.

"Did you see me jerking in the meeting this morning?" I asked.

"Well, yes, I did," John responded.

"I need to be removed from this job," I said. "It is causing me to twitch uncontrollably. I'm asking you for health reasons."

This man, who had seemed to be sympathetic, was now fairly stern. He agreed to see what he could do for me. Several weeks passed, and nothing was done about the job to ease my condition. It was basically ignored for some time.

Months later I asked again, and he said that he was still looking into it. The job was too important to let go, so I would have to do it until he found another place for me. Finally I resolved it by taking a medical leave. I was gone for a little over a month.

When I returned, the job that was so important had been completely untouched. No one had looked after it or had done anything with it.

Nothing had changed. Since I had more than thirty years in with the company and could leave with a full retirement, I just wanted to get out. I called Mr. Wiseman and told him that is what I wanted to do. I quickly received a letter in the mail from him informing me that he could not take my case.

I was knocked off my feet again, and left outside in the rain. I fretted, paced, went to my computer and drafted a two-column paper headed Blend vs. Wiseman. I listed my points of the case against his views. I faxed it to him immediately. I paced and fretted some more, and then called him.

"What do you mean you don't want to take my case?" I said.

"If you retire, the case won't have any grounds," he said. "We seem to have some differences of opinion here, and I just can't take the case."

Bud Wiseman was both amused and pleased with this correspondence of opposing viewpoints. He was glad to see some spunk and was also amazed by my aggressiveness. He agreed to again work with me if I didn't retire. From that time on, I clearly voiced my opinion, even when differing from his. He seemed to gain a lot of respect for me. I provided him with his arguments for the case, and did as much of the work as possible myself at the direction of Gwenn.

Bud Wiseman did not appreciate Gwenn like I did. Sometimes he wished that I would not have listened to her. I followed her guidance carefully. From her training in the police force, she taught me defense tactics; such as, how not to back away from someone who was attacking me, but to move closer into their comfort zone to make them uncomfortable. She never directed me wrong.

In December of 1994, during the work break of the holiday season, Howard Thiesen III was served as part of a lawsuit titled "Ellen Blend vs. General Motors Corporation and Howard Thiesen III."

Finally, a change of job came through for me, and my days became more palatable. This time I was given the responsibility of monitoring engineering changes. I now worked with a lot of engineers and also closely with Barbara Moore.

Barbara was a haughty lady who I learned to admire. She lived to appreciate the better things in life with her retired husband, and at work she was opinionative, free-spoken, and avoided by many of the men. She was often smarter than they were, and they preferred not to have to deal with her.

The nervous twitches continued, but were less bothersome. I had a discussion with Matt regarding them since he now worked in the medical field. He told me that my central nervous system had been damaged and that it generally was permanent.

"Let's hope that it isn't," he stated.

I continued to meet with the lawyer several evenings after work to discuss various aspects of development in the lawsuit. We compiled a list of people who were significant supporters and contenders to the case. All of these people would be deposed. We tried to cover what we thought each of them would say under oath, but could not determine how their statements would actually be verbalized.

Co-workers, hearing about my situation, came to my defense. Many were more than willing to provide me with documentation and facts that I would not have learned otherwise. I continued to include these things in my ongoing pages of documentation.

I had telephone calls from some that I hardly had dealings with previously. Several had such a vengeance built up against the corporation that they were more than willing to voluntarily dig for information for me. Barbara brought in stacks of corporate benefit handbooks that she had saved from years back, as she felt that they would support me in my rights. Files were being copied of organizational changes that were being made and brought to me.

Each time something happened to any friend or relative working for the corporation, even outside the immediate office building, I was notified. I had a crowd cheering me on. They all wanted me to get back at the corporation for all of the wrong doings that had happened to them throughout the years. The support was staggering and immeasurable.

Both Barbara Moore and Carolyn Bartell were extremely capable of finding out every rumor and miniscule happening that was going on in the corporation. If you wanted to know anything, you just had to ask either one of them.

I had been warned not to trust anyone during this period. Gwenn alerted me that someone would come to me as a friend, but would really be seeking information. She cautioned me to say nothing.

"Do not tell anyone what is going on, no matter how close you are with them," she warned. "Watch for this person to appear. It will happen."

I was to learn what it felt like to be really stupid. My telephone rang. It was a fellow I had worked with in my previous assignment under Linda O'Claire. Everybody liked Sam Coletta. The Godfather, they would call him. Sam would occasionally take some of the girls to lunch.

This call was to invite me to lunch sometime. He would get back with me later in the week.

"Fine," I said. I was pleased, never suspecting a thing. Instead of calling me back, he stopped by my office. He sat on the desk right next to where I was working.

He began by pretending to confide in me.

"Did you hear what happened to some of the guys in my department?" he asked.

At that moment, I was not thinking about what department he worked for, and said "No."

"Well," he began, "Some of them lost their eighth levels. Can you believe that?"

Of course I knew that and told him so. My thoughts were buzzing, wondering if he already knew that I had also been a victim.

"Anything like that happen around here?" he asked.

"It happened to me, Sam," I said, as I continued to work.

"To you?" he played along. "Why?" he asked.

"I really don't know, Sam."

"I wouldn't let 'em get away with that," he resounded. "I'd sue the pants off 'em. I wouldn't let 'em get away with that. I hope you have a good lawyer," he said.

"I do," I admitted coolly.

"But do you have a labor law lawyer?" he asked.

"Yes I do," I continued non-chalantly.

"Boy! I would certainly sue the pants off of 'em if I were you," he continued.

I said nothing.

"You do have a labor law lawyer, though, huh?" he continued to pursue his question.

"Do you mean a labor lawyer?" I asked.

"Yeah. You have one though, huh?" he tried to verify.

"I have one," I said.

By evening it all hit home. I felt really stupid. I reviewed the entire conversation over and over again in my mind. I paced in my kitchen until I thought Gwenn would be home from work. Then I called her to tell her how really stupid I had been. I was just grateful that I hadn't volunteered any additional information. She was easy on me.

I never said hello to that man again. I ignored him each time that I passed him in the hallway. I was so angry that he would pose as a friend.

Another surprising element happened. I was called by a Jake Fruen who worked in a manufacturing capacity. He said that he had a copy of my resume, had an opening, and wanted to meet with me. We scheduled the time for an interview. In conversation, he mentioned that the job was for a managerial-level position in Body Formation.

I was interviewed by two gentlemen. I cautiously asked about the position level, just to be sure that I understood the job for which I was interviewing. I was trying to figure out if this group was aware of my having been demoted. They weren't. I was shown an organization chart for the position that was open, and it was clearly an eighth-level assignment.

A week or so later, I was visited by Jake Fruen. This group was part of the old regime of assembly plant guys that definitely had a heart and soul. It was probably what I liked best about manufacturing, and no doubt why I fared so well in that environment.

Jake stated that he just wanted to stop by personally. He wanted to let me know that even though my skills were quite good for the job, they had found someone else that had better tooling experience.

I thanked him for his kindness in responding to me personally. He said that he would certainly keep me in mind for something in the future. I knew he meant that. That was how most manufacturing people were.

Incidentally, the term "bottom feeders," referring to low-level producers in his organization, came from one of the new regime of manufacturing managers.

I was disappointed not to have pulled off that coup d'état, but in retrospect it probably wouldn't have worked anyway. When it finally reached my heads of staff or the Personnel office, Jake Fruen and his group would have been tipped off. I would have been blackballed and frozen in my spot.

Part III

Chapter Eleven

I Was Reclassified

My daughter, Sue, was to be married toward the end of July. Gwenn asked how she was coming along with her wedding plans. I told her fine, and that she was busy getting the bridesmaids all fitted; the flowers had all been taken care of; and the cake had been ordered.

"Is her dress ready?" Gwenn asked.

"She has another fitting next week," I said.

At Gwenn's direction, I had sent letters to the President of the Corporation as well as the Board of Directors. Since they had been informed of what had happened, they were now liable and able to be deposed in my case.

When the response came back from the corporation, it gave Bud Wiseman a hardy laugh. The letter read like this:

> In response to your letter sent to the President and Board of Directors, please be advised that the corporate Open Door Policy is only open if there is an involuntary termination of employment. Your request will be addressed by Mr. Les Weaver of your division.

I didn't request anything. According to Gwenn I merely informed them of their legal liability!

Bud Wiseman laughed hysterically because the Open Door Policy was only open if you didn't work there!

Since I still hadn't received an answer to my letter of reasons for my demotion, I sat at my laptop computer and wrote another letter to Les Weaver. I referenced the letter from Corporate Personnel that stated he would be getting in contact with me.

Still not getting a response, another letter dated March of 1994 followed. It stated, "Sufficient time has elapsed without any communication. I am requesting on what date I will receive notification and documentation regarding my demotion of November 1, 1993." I am sure that I gave a stated time period in which I expected a returned communication.

Finally a response came. It was placed on my desk at work, and I found it upon returning from lunch. It said:

> I would like to apologize for any misunderstanding in regard to the action taken on November 1, 1993. I take exception to your statement in asking for notification and documentation in regard to your demotion. This action was to reclassify you in accordance with your job responsibilities. Appropriate explanation has been given by your supervisor and no further action is required on the part of management.

That evening I read the letter to Gwenn and asked her what she thought.

"Write him back," she ordered.

"Saying what?" I asked.

"Tell him you are concerned for his taking exception to your asking for notification and documentation in regard to your demotion of November 1, 1993, and the fact that you were reclassified. Ask for his written rationale for the action that was taken. Tell him that you want it by month's end."

A couple of weeks passed, and my letter was again answered. I had also asked what my title and salary range was. It took them four months for them to tell me that I was an entry-level Staff Assistant! They did not address why the action was taken, but it stated my new code and salary range with minimum, midpoint and maximum figures. It also stated that it was the *only* documentation that existed regarding the reclassification.

I was instructed by Gwenn to put it with the rest of my documentation and to be sure that I locked it up.

"Here at home?" I asked.

"It's not a bad idea," she said. "You never know who could befriend you and take information that you need."

I told her that I could really get paranoid about this. She reminded me that it pays to be careful.

"Trust me," she said. "Even if you're out socially, they could still send someone to you to find out information."

"Really!" I exclaimed.

"Sure. If they know that you and Matt aren't doing well, they could find a Matt look-alike and set him up to meet you in some social setting. Then he could win your trust and you might confide in him."

"I can't believe it. They would really go that far?" I asked.

"If there's information they want badly enough," she said.

"I won't be able to let my guard down anywhere," I said.

"I'm just telling you to be careful. Have I ever told you wrong?"

I had to admit—never!

Matt, the gentleman I had been dating for a very long time, was becoming uncomfortable in the relationship. We had broken up many times before, but normally gravitated back together again. He had tried to make the break again recently but just could never bring himself to follow though with it.

We had a lovely evening and morning together and were sitting at the kitchen table. I had my usual cup of coffee and he a Diet Coke. Discussion again centered around him needing to take an intermission from the relationship, but that he didn't seem to be doing it. He told me that he so enjoyed our time together that it was difficult to leave. However, he felt that he really needed some time by himself.

A little in anger I said, "Well, what is it? Is it an intermission or isn't it?"

"It's an intermission," he said. "I guess I should just do it."

I asked why it was that he felt he needed one. He said that he wasn't sure; he just felt compelled to do it. He kissed me good-bye, and we again parted.

At work John Nelson called me into his office for a meeting. He was actually passing out raises for the past year and I received one.

"In order to get the full amount, you would have to take more of a leadership role and go beyond your assignment," he stated. "I admit that might be an unfair assessment based on your situation."

"Why do I get one at all?" I asked.

"Because you're seen as a good entry-level manager, so you get an increase. I need you to fill out your appraisal forms, too," and he started to hand me the forms.

"I won't be participating in the appraisal process," I said.

Defensively, he said, "Shall I write on there that you won't participate?"

"No," I said. "I'll write it on there myself. There is no point in my filling out appraisal forms when management surely didn't use them to demote me."

"That was just because managerial-level job requirements have changed, and you're seen as a good entry-level manager. Don't you have any goals you'd like to write in there?" he asked.

"Sure I have goals. But the appraisals are ludicrous and have no meaning. They're simply rhetoric."

Again John asked for clarification. "Why won't you participate in the process?"

"Where was management's responsibility in using the appraisal system to let me know that I wasn't performing to their expectations? I had no opportunity to correct a deficiency."

Stepping away from responsibility, John Nelson stated "That's between you and Howard. Don't you have any goals or objectives you want to pursue?"

"You know what I want," I said.

"Well, if it's an early retirement, I can't do anything like that for you; but you should have a plan."

"Oh, I have a plan all right. When Howard Thiesen can promote a male, under the age of 40, into the position that he originally offered to me, don't tell me that this paperwork has any validity. I was equally qualified for that position."

"In your opinion," he stated.

"Yes, in my opinion," I countered.

"Maybe you should look at yourself in the mirror. Maybe you perceive yourself differently than others do."

"I look in the mirror every day of my life," I said

"Then you still want to pursue the matter through legal means?" he asked.

I was terribly wounded at this point. "Absolutely. You know it's already in process."

"Well, it may not turn out as you expect," he offered. "What do you think the company car is worth?"

"Minimally $8,000 a year," I replied.

"I think your estimate is too high," he said.

I was quick to react. "You could estimate my driving a small compact, or you could estimate my driving a luxury vehicle. I would be happy to tell you what I've been driving!"

He softened. "You don't have to fill out the appraisal forms if you don't want to. I know you'll do whatever I ask of you and you'll do a good job."

"Thanks, John," I said and left his office.

It was now lunchtime, and I was on my way to pick up a friend. My car was struck by another vehicle backing out of a parking space. It hit my passing car while still on the work premises. That was to add to my list of inconveniences.

I was now at the point in my case where mediation had taken place, and an amount was set that was thought to be what my case was worth. I was informed of the results by Bud Wiseman. He also informed me of the risks of not accepting mediation.

"If you refuse to accept the amount of the mediators, and you lose the case, you will be responsible for all court costs. It is quite a risk, and I encourage you to consider this."

Bud Wiseman was also kind enough to introduce me to the judge and to get his opinion as to the outcome of many of the cases in Macomb County. The judge was of the opinion that most were not decided favorably on the part of the plaintiff, and that I should weigh these factors carefully.

The next time I spoke to Bud Wiseman, he, of course, wanted to know if I had decided to accept or reject mediation. I had not decided.

Later that day he called me to tell me that he had heard from Alex White of Personnel.

"Oh, what did he have to say?" I asked.

"He is so condescending," said Bud. "They really think they can't be touched. Screw it. We're going for it!"

Bud Wiseman decided that I was not accepting the mediation! I was okay with that decision.

In my private single life, I had attended a dance and met a very attractive man who asked for my telephone number. His name was Steve Olde, and he called me on Monday evening and asked me to go out on Saturday night. I was excited, soon became crazy about him, and his sense of humor was exactly what I needed.

He was an attorney, himself, but we really did not get into the aspects of my case. He could see that I clearly had it under control and did not need his assistance.

When I returned to work after the first of the year, an invitation came to me directly from Bob White of the Legal Staff. I was being asked to attend a Validation Meeting for the work I had done on his program of managing the timing of glove box contents. He told me that John Nelson was also being invited and that he had agreed that I could attend.

John Nelson and I went to the meeting together. After a few brief exchanged greetings with the people that I knew, we sat down. The meeting began shortly, and Bob White began speaking.

"This meeting today is to express thanks to all of the participants in this project. It has been termed a 'grand success.' It was a grand success because of our contributions in getting our part done right and on time. I think we should go down the row, here, and let each of the participants tell about their part. We don't need to be so formal here."

Bob White sat down, and Jerry Folberg stood up and began to direct the meeting.

"Let's start with you, Jeanie."

Jeanie was a middle-aged woman who worked in the Legal Group. "Well, I'd like to speak about the success of the Design Review Meeting last week. It was such a success because all of our vehicles had all of the information there, and we were very organized."

The group applauded lightly. The next person seated next to Jeanie was Laura Casey from Paper Validation.

"I, too, have great things to say about the project outcome. Never before have we had everything at a car show on time."

Again, the group applauded lightly.

Next, Doug Allman spoke. "Speaking from a data management perspective, I also want to compliment the improvement made in our ability to have all of the owner's manuals updated in a timely manner. This was all due to the efficiencies of the information that was collected. All owner's manuals were at Pilot, and on time, but some of the portfolio information, like the cassettes and pens, were not." He directed his conversation at me.

I was quick to ask, "Did the timing plans that I developed make any impact? Were there any improvements?"

From elsewhere in the room, Tim Newton spoke up.

"Yes. They were invaluable. Under no uncertain terms; I want to make that perfectly clear."

Further defending my position, "I'm sure it would have been better had someone been able to monitor each groups contents to the end to see that this information got there on time."

There were undertones of concurrence among the group. Jerry Folberg interjected. "The only real glitch we had was that one of the cars in the show did not have a radio in it to be validated, but that really did not reflect on our job. Actually, getting the cars there on time continues to be a problem. That would be another area that could be worked on. Both of these situations could be improved with a person monitoring the project."

The meeting broke, and I was caught by one of the participants, Laura Casey. "You really did a great job with this project, Ellen," she said.

"Why, thanks, Laura."

"I mean that. The quality of the work that was done by you personally was really noticed by our group."

"I'm pleased to hear that." After the beatings I had taken over the last year, I was quick to add, "That makes me feel really good."

Chapter Twelve

Depositions Take Place

Bud Wiseman and I met for breakfast prior to the start of depositions. I was pretty nervous about them, and he had asked that we meet there to advise me of what would take place.

"There will be some things that you won't want to hear, but the important thing is not to let on and say nothing. Don't react to any of these comments. It's important that you don't," he instructed. "Don't volunteer any information, either. Just answer their questions."

It was now March of 1995 and Bud Wiseman and I entered the law offices of the attorney hired by General Motors. Everyone was seated around a large conference table. The attorney representing General Motors and two inside-General Motors' attorneys were present. Also present was Howard Thiesen III. I was sworn in and the questioning began by Mike Hanley, General Motors' attorney.

> MIKE HANLEY
> Raise your right hand. Do you solemnly
> swear to speak the truth, the whole truth,
> so help you God.
>
> ELLEN
> I do.

MIKE HANLEY
Please state your full name.

ELLEN
Ellen Marie Blend.

MIKE HANLEY
Where were you born?

ELLEN
Detroit, Michigan.

MIKE HANLEY
For the record, your full address . . .

The general questions continued, and then a break took place for lunch. Bud Wiseman and I walked down the street and got a sandwich at a nearby restaurant.

I told Bud Wiseman how really draining this was. He assured me that I was doing fine, but said I didn't have to tell them that I was a supervisor of people all the times that I was. I told him that I knew he didn't want me to, but I couldn't help myself. I wanted them to know just whom they were really dealing with, and I wanted it on record. We finished lunch and returned to the conference room.

Back at work, Barbara Moore approached me about my case. She stated that she didn't really believe in discrimination, so she didn't think she would help my case. Her conversation made me understand that she had been deposed and was a little unhappy about it. I confirmed that she had been notified to report, and then told her that if she didn't want to give a deposition she didn't have to. I would have her removed from the list.

She acknowledged that she would prefer that, and I had her dismissed from the list as agreed.

Before our conversation was over, however, she stated that if she were called for deposition she would have to say that Howard Thiesen was an incompetent manager. I was surprised at that, but she definitely had her own opinions.

She then asked me if I knew that Howard Thiesen was getting a transfer. I told her that I had heard.

Some might think his transfer was to remove him from the current talk about the case, but I personally felt they knew he had discriminated against enough women and had better get him out of there.

Barbara then humorously stated that maybe he and I could share a going away cake together! She always did make me smile.

Later on, Carolyn Bartell stopped in to see me. She wanted to share that Ken Centurion's job was going to be changing.

I asked her if she meant the Timing Core job. She did. She said they were going to have to assign all of the Timing Managers to him to save his job. There was a new edict that all eighth-level managers had to have people reporting to them.

I just shook my head about that one. They always protected those they wanted to.

She continued to say that she had heard that Harry Cardine just got an early retirement. That surprised me as I didn't think he was any older than I was, and they wouldn't give me one. It turns out he was the same age as myself, and he was given a retirement package. This was another point of discrimination.

At the next Howard Thiesen staff meeting, I again brazenly took a seat directly across from him and stared right into his face.

The next set of depositions was to take place back at the law offices of the attorney General Motors had selected. The first deposition was that of Howard Thiesen III. I was much calmer that day knowing that I was not going to get interrogated; and besides, I was feeling somewhat confident. This was my day to enjoy others' answering of questions.

> BUD WISEMAN
> Please state your age for the record.

> HOWARD THIESEN III
> I'm forty-two years old.

> BUD WISEMAN
> What school and level did you go to?

> HOWARD THIESEN III
> LaSalle, Michigan, a satellite, Masters
> degree.

BUD WISEMAN
Give me your work background, starting
with the year you were hired.

The questioning continued and all expressions in the
room were stern.

BUD WISEMAN
And you were a part of the demotion of
Ellen Blend?

HOWARD THIESEN III
Yes I was.

BUD WISEMAN
And did you feel her work was not
adequate?

HOWARD THIESEN III
Her job was changed due to a reduction
in workforce. There was a lot of
reorganization going on and I had no
additional openings available for her.
Work performance was a secondary
implication.

BUD WISEMAN
And you were aware of a letter written
about Ellen's performance?

HOWARD THIESEN III
Yes; it was written by Scott Warner.

BUD WISEMAN
And did you talk with anyone about this letter?

HOWARD THIESEN III
Yes, I did.

BUD WISEMAN
With whom did you speak?

HOWARD THIESEN III
I had conversations with some
employees. It was Robert Levin, Linda
O'Claire, Curt Russo, Ken Centurion--I
don't remember specifically.
Cumulatively, there were problems on
the car group that she worked for.

BUD WISEMAN
And she worked directly for you for a time?

HOWARD THIESEN III
Yes, she did. She replaced Phil Goodwin of
my staff.

BUD WISEMAN
And what level was Phil Goodwin?

HOWARD THIESEN III
He was an eighth level. The job could
have been a seventh- or eighth-level job,
and she worked for Karen Dawson.
Karen was a part-time employee.

BUD WISEMAN
Why is it that Karen worked part-time?

HOWARD THIESEN III
She requested to.

BUD WISEMAN
Do you like Ellen Blend?

HOWARD THIESEN III
I have nothing to do with Ellen Blend.

BUD WISEMAN
Do you or does anyone else have a
problem with Ellen's personality?

HOWARD THIESEN III
I don't recall anyone saying she had a
poor personality.

BUD WISEMAN
Is it true that at one time you offered her
a Timing Core position?

HOWARD THIESEN III
I did not assign it to her. I felt it was best
for her to stay in Industrial Engineering and
stay with one career path.

BUD WISEMAN
Did you counsel her regarding her
performance?

HOWARD THIESEN III
I reviewed her appraisals--prior

appraisals, that is.

BUD WISEMAN
Was there anything negative on her
appraisals?

HOWARD THIESEN III
Not overtly negative.

BUD WISEMAN
What percentage did you attach to her
performance that related directly to the
memo that was written by Scott Warner?

HOWARD THIESEN III
I wouldn't have known a performance
problem existed.

BUD WISEMAN
How is it that you came upon this memo?

HOWARD THIESEN III
A copy was passed on to me in a
supervisor's file, not a personnel file.

BUD WISEMAN
Do all employees have a supervisor's file?

HOWARD THIESEN III
No.

BUD WISEMAN
Were her past appraisals positive?

HOWARD THIESEN III
I couldn't say.

BUD WISEMAN
Did you work with her regarding her
performance?

HOWARD THIESEN III
No.

BUD WISEMAN
Is it your perception that she can do
managerial-level work?

HOWARD THIESEN III
Yes. There have been no managerial-
level openings. I looked at nine or ten
that would have been a good fit, but
none were open.

BUD WISEMAN
You recently promoted Ken Centurion
into a managerial-level job?

HOWARD THIESEN III
Yes I did. I promoted him from a
seventh-level Timing Manager to an
eighth-level Timing Core Manager.

BUD WISEMAN
Were there others who were also
promoted by you?

HOWARD THIESEN III
Yes. I can't remember all of those.

BUD WISEMAN
How long was Ken Centurion employed
by General Motors?

HOWARD THIESEN III
I don't remember. But Ken had much
more timing experience. His whole
career was in systems and timing, even
before he came to General Motors. He
worked for a consulting firm and came
here in the mid-eighties.

BUD WISEMAN
Have you done anything socially with
Ken Centurion?

HOWARD THIESEN III
Yes, a Christmas party, once.

BUD WISEMAN
How old is Ken Centurion?

HOWARD THIESEN III
He's in his mid-thirties.

BUD WISEMAN
I have some exhibits here, sixteen
documents. This first one, the letter
written by Scott Warner. Did you talk
with any of these individuals copied?

HOWARD THIESEN III
Who?

BUD WISEMAN
Robert Levin?

HOWARD THIESEN III
No.

BUD WISEMAN
Dan Quarton?

HOWARD THIESEN III
No.

BUD WISEMAN
Derek Armstrong?

HOWARD THIESEN III
No.

BUD WISEMAN
Dick Landerman?

HOWARD THIESEN III
No.

BUD WISEMAN
This letter was written on March 20, 1992. And there was no demotion until November of 1993. Is that right?

HOWARD THIESEN III
Yes.

BUD WISEMAN
What is the process to determine if there
are any suitable openings for an
employee?

HOWARD THIESEN III
It is policy to talk to Personnel and ask
if there are any openings. They help
determine the best position and then
Personnel takes the advice of the
supervisor.

BUD WISEMAN
Is it true that Ellen Blend occasionally
experienced a mental block?

Bud Wiseman was referring to the letter written by Scott
Warner that implied that sometimes I had periods of
inability to complete thoughts. In reality, I was
stultified. I had been left speechless and refrained from
saying what was really on my mind.

HOWARD THIESEN III
No.

BUD WISEMAN
Did she sometimes demonstrate periods
of confusion?

HOWARD THIESEN III
No. The only work she did for me was
on the business plan.

BUD WISEMAN
Who took care of the data on the

business plan?

HOWARD THIESEN III
Ellen.

BUD WISEMAN
Was Karen Dawson part of that job?

HOWARD THIESEN III
No.

BUD WISEMAN
Didn't Karen know what she was doing
on that job?

HOWARD THIESEN III
Maybe.   Karen and Ellen made
corrections to the data.

BUD WISEMAN
Did Robert Levin supervise Ellen Blend?

HOWARD THIESEN III
Yes.

BUD WISEMAN
Did he speak to her about her
performance?

HOWARD THIESEN III
Not that I know of.

BUD WISEMAN
How about Dick Landerman or Ed

Worthington?

HOWARD THIESEN III
I spoke to Ed Worthington after Ellen
was reclassified. That did not play a
role in her reclassification.

BUD WISEMAN
Did you speak with either Personnel
people, Les Weaver or Alex White
about reclassifying Ellen Blend?

HOWARD THIESEN III
No.

BUD WISEMAN
Why is that?

HOWARD THIESEN III
I didn't want to share 'dirty laundry.'

BUD WISEMAN
Didn't Ellen ask to be considered for the
Capacity Planning job?

HOWARD THIESEN III
Yes. She wasn't as qualified as Clayton
O'Connor.

BUD WISEMAN
How is it you know of Clayton
O'Connor's capabilities?

HOWARD THIESEN III
I met with him once a week as Timing

112

Manager.

BUD WISEMAN
And how about Ken Centurion. How did you know of his work?

HOWARD THIESEN III
Also at the weekly timing meetings.

BUD WISEMAN
What level was the Capacity Planning position before and after Clayton O'Connor took it?

HOWARD THIESEN III
I don't know.

BUD WISEMAN
Did you anticipate problems with Ellen's performance?

HOWARD THIESEN III
Her problems were in the Program Timing group. Her carryover responsibilities were diminishing.

BUD WISEMAN
Did you assist Ellen in getting any other interviews outside of your group?

HOWARD THIESEN III
Yes. She interviewed with an Industrial Engineering group.

A break took place and Bud Wiseman and I went into one of the back offices to discuss that morning's questions and answers. It was now mid-July of 1995.

I exclaimed "Wow, what a day this is going to be."

He agreed, but assured me that we were doing well. He was great at summarizing what just took place and spoke into a tape recorder for his personal record.

"The deposition of Howard Thiesen III was just taken on July 15, 1995. His position was . . . "

We went back into the conference room with Clayton O'Connor now to be seated for questioning. He was generally felt to be unsuitable for management among the talk of the women employees.

BUD WISEMAN
State your name for the record, please.

CLAYTON O'CONNOR
Clayton O'Connor.

BUD WISEMAN
And what is your education level?

CLAYTON O'CONNOR
I'm twelve credits towards a Masters--
half way through. I started three years
ago.

BUD WISEMAN
And please give us your history with

General Motors.

CLAYTON O'CONNOR
Well, I left General Motors and went to
Nebraska. Than I came back and
worked at Chevrolet at the axle plant,
then engine plant.

BUD WISEMAN
What was your position and level at the
axle plant?

CLAYTON O'CONNOR
I was a Line Supervisor. That was in
the late sixties, as a sixth level.

BUD WISEMAN
How long were you there?

CLAYTON O'CONNOR
One year. Then I went to the engine
plant. I was a Supervisor, and
supervised fifty-two people on line. I
was a Foreman and Supervisor at the
same time.

BUD WISEMAN
I understand that you later were moved into
a clerk's position. How did that happen?

CLAYTON O'CONNOR
That was at my request. I was a Clerk and
Maintenance Dispatcher. I later became
Office Manager and had four clerks
working for me. That was in the late

seventies.

BUD WISEMAN
What did you do next?

CLAYTON O'CONNOR
I worked for the Fiero plant in Pontiac until 1981. I started as a layout engineer of the offices and indirect labor, then was an entry-level I.E. Supervisor. I then became a Planning Administrator and was responsible for hourly and salaried employees for both Prototype and Pilot. That was until 1988, and then I came to work here as a Planning Analyst.

BUD WISEMAN
Who did you work for here?

CLAYTON O'CONNOR
I worked for Roger Benton, then Don Milton for a year, and was promoted to an eighth level in about July or September.

BUD WISEMAN
Did you supervise anyone?

CLAYTON O'CONNOR
Yes, I had an assistant. Later, when I took on the responsibility for three car lines, I had three people working for me. Ellen Blend worked for me in late 1992 and part of 1993.

BUD WISEMAN
Did you have any problems with Ellen
while she was working for you?

CLAYTON O'CONNOR
Yes, I had problems. I spoke to her
about ten times.

BUD WISEMAN
Was there ever anything put in writing?

CLAYTON O'CONNOR
No.

BUD WISEMAN
What problems were there?

Good ol' Clayton was pleased to have the opportunity to
slam me. It was the first he could get the upper hand.

CLAYTON O'CONNOR
Oh, inability to develop work plans with
the network as required, and refusal to
do work she considered wasted effort.

BUD WISEMAN
Was it inability or refusal?

Clayton O'Connor continued to enjoy his powerful
position.

CLAYTON O'CONNOR
She never showed me she could do the
work. You must have an understanding
of manufacturing and engineering and

how events stay together.

BUD WISEMAN
What training did she receive?

CLAYTON O'CONNOR
I'm not aware of any training.

BUD WISEMAN
Did you talk to Personnel about Ellen?

CLAYTON O'CONNOR
Yes, several times.

BUD WISEMAN
With whom did you speak?

CLAYTON O'CONNOR
I can't remember the gal's name, but it
wasn't Diane Hillsdale.

BUD WISEMAN
Did you tell Ellen that you talked to
Personnel?

CLAYTON O'CONNOR
No, but I told her several times they were
trying to find another position for her.

BUD WISEMAN
How is it that Ellen left working for you?

CLAYTON O'CONNOR
Another program needed help.

BUD WISEMAN
Did Howard Thiesen ask you about Ellen?

CLAYTON O'CONNOR
Yes.

BUD WISEMAN
How many times did you talk about her?

CLAYTON O'CONNOR
About two or three times, maximum.

BUD WISEMAN
Did you interview for the Capacity Planning job?

CLAYTON O'CONNOR
No.

BUD WISEMAN
Had you ever done capacity planning work before?

CLAYTON O'CONNOR
No.

BUD WISEMAN
Isn't it true that you and another gentleman, Bob Ricker, changed jobs with each other?

CLAYTON O'CONNOR
Yes.

BUD WISEMAN
Why was that?

CLAYTON O'CONNOR
I don't know.

BUD WISEMAN
Wasn't Bob a seventh level?

CLAYTON O'CONNOR
I don't know.

BUD WISEMAN
And didn't you stay in an eighth-level
position when you took the job?

CLAYTON O'CONNOR
Yes, I did.

Again it was break time and Bud Wiseman and I
reviewed what had just transpired and he made
epigrammatic statements into his tape recorder. He
asked me what I thought about the last deposition.

I said that Clayton was sure using his opportunity for
power and that he was lying. He was taking every
opportunity to knock me.

Bud Wiseman agreed that he was, but said he didn't
seem that strong. I agreed that he was not.

Everyone reconvened in the conference room and it was
back to the questioning . Robert Levin was the next to
be deposed. He headed the Business Team for the car

group for which I had previously worked.

BUD WISEMAN
Did you have an opportunity to directly observe Ellen's work?

ROBERT LEVIN
She was part of a Business Team.

BUD WISEMAN
How often did you interact with her?

ROBERT LEVIN
Well, the Business Team had about ten people on it, but many times there were about thirty people in the room.

BUD WISEMAN
Did you ever interact with her one on one?

ROBERT LEVIN
On a few occasions.

BUD WISEMAN
Did Ellen have the technical knowledge of car program timing?

ROBERT LEVIN
She could recite more about the generic car integration, critical path, etc.

BUD WISEMAN
What training did she have?

ROBERT LEVIN
I don't know. There was no formal training. Just template guidelines.

BUD WISEMAN
Did you voice any concerns to her? Any specifics about her work?

ROBERT LEVIN
No. I had some complaints from Dick Landerman. I did not solicit him. He had to integrate a new product and expressed supportive concern.

BUD WISEMAN
Would you say that Ellen had a lack of technical knowledge? Or intellectual ability?

ROBERT LEVIN
Intellectual ability to do the job? Let's just say that it was 'difficult for her.'

BUD WISEMAN
How was it 'difficult for her'?

ROBERT LEVIN
She relied on engineers to do her job. I had indications from others plus myself, and asked Scott Warner to determine what the problems were.

BUD WISEMAN
Were there memos requested on any

other individuals?

ROBERT LEVIN
Not that I'm aware of. I asked Scott Warner's perception of Ellen's performance. He went to Dick Landerman and got an opinion. He shared the memo with Dick. I don't recall his comments, but he was very supportive.

BUD WISEMAN
Did you have any contact with Ellen Blend after the memo was written?

ROBERT LEVIN
No.

BUD WISEMAN
I understand there were other demotions in the staff, other than your group. How did these demotions come about?

ROBERT LEVIN
They took place in the HRM meetings. People's names were put on a list, and we were asked for opinions as to whether or not they were doing a good job. It was a consensus on the part of the staff. I was part of that. It was stated, unless you have an objection, this person will be demoted.

BUD WISEMAN
Did you say anything?

ROBERT LEVIN
I don't recall.

BUD WISEMAN
Did anyone ask you specifically if Ellen
should be demoted?

ROBERT LEVIN
No.

BUD WISEMAN
Are you aware of any other demotions?

ROBERT LEVIN
There were some in Quality and some in
Engineering. Kurt Hathaway was
changed from an eighth level to a
seventh level, and then back to an eighth
level.

BUD WISEMAN
What transpired to do that?

ROBERT LEVIN
His performance was minimal. He was
moved to another job opening and his
level was changed.

BUD WISEMAN
Why is it that he was changed back to a
managerial-level?

ROBERT LEVIN
He was a Certified Quality Engineer,
and he found another job that was eighth
level.

At the next break when Bud Wiseman and I went over
the depositions just taken, he commented that Robert
Levin was pretty egotistical.

I agreed, and said besides that he lied! He never talked
or met with me once since the time I stayed after the
meeting to introduce myself!

Bud Wiseman was surprised. I told him that I never
interacted with the man, so how would he know if the
job was 'difficult for me'?

We then went to lunch on his statement that we could
talk further there.

After lunch we returned to the conference room. The
afternoon began with Ken Centurion's deposition.

BUD WISEMAN
I understand you were promoted to the
Timing Core position as an eighth level?

KEN CENTURION
Yes, I was.

BUD WISEMAN
And what are your duties? Are they for
a particular car group?

KEN CENTURION
No. No specific car program. I'm
expected to do hires and train new
timing managers, promote new
divisional issues, maintain the generic
template and definitions.

BUD WISEMAN
Do you supervise anyone?

KEN CENTURION
Yes, one person. The secretary for the
department.

BUD WISEMAN
How is it that you got this position?

KEN CENTURION
I was informed on May 29. I was told
by Howard Thiesen.

BUD WISEMAN
Were there any other candidates?

KEN CENTURION
No.

BUD WISEMAN
Were there any other people other than
Ellen that were unhappy about this?

KEN CENTURION
Yes. Carolyn Bartell, Sylvia Tanner,
Suzanne Johnson.

BUD WISEMAN
Do you know Scott Warner?

KEN CENTURION
No.

BUD WISEMAN
Did you ever see any documents
regarding Ellen Blend's performance?

KEN CENTURION
No.

BUD WISEMAN
Did anyone ever speak to you about
having a problem with her performance?

KEN CENTURION
One time, with Don Milton. There was
a problem with the car group, not a
problem with Ellen Blend. It was a
casual comment.

BUD WISEMAN
That will be all. Thank you for coming.

Other dispositions followed including that of Kurt
Hathaway. Kurt basically backtracked his way up the
management chain of command stating that he had his
certification as a Quality Engineer, an accomplishment
not held by others in his field. With each question posed
to him in the deposition as to what each level of
management told him, his answer was, "Same thing."

Basically, each had told him that it was the decision of his employing division. He evidently pushed hard enough and on enough people until he found a hole in the system and was able to be reclassified back to his eighth-level position. I secretly wondered what threats he may have made that worked.

On the way out of the law offices, Bud Wiseman and I crossed the street on our way to our cars. He stated, "You may have been good at what you did, but maybe not as good as you thought you were."

"What do you mean?" I said. "Did you believe all of those lies under oath?"

"Maybe I did," said Wiseman. "That Levin guy. He was pretty convincing."

I was awfully hurt about this, alarmed at how he had sized up the elements of the case at this juncture, and terribly disappointed.

"Well, he and Clayton both lied today. I'm sorry that you believed them," I said. I drove home wounded and upset.

Chapter Thirteen

Ladies Day in Court

It was the second day of Bud Wiseman taking depositions. He and the other attorneys and myself were seated at the large conference table along with the court reporter.

Carolyn was a flashy blonde, and entered with a fire-red dress on, making her debut. Bud Wiseman was charmed by her overly friendly and presumptuous stature. She addressed the people already in the room as she made her grand, informal entrance. She was giggling and smiling.

CAROLYN BARTELL
I thought I'd wear a 'power dress' today.

I returned her smile. She had always been pretty good about supporting me.

BUD WISEMAN
State your name for the reporter please.

CAROLYN BARTELL
Carolyn Bartell.

BUD WISEMAN
And your educational background?

CAROLYN BARTELL
I have a Bachelor's in elementary
education and a Master's from Central
Michigan.

BUD WISEMAN
When did you start working for General
Motors?

CAROLYN BARTELL
I started in February of 1978. I was a
teacher for a year and a sub before that.

BUD WISEMAN
And did you apply for the Timing Core
position?

CAROLYN BARTELL
Yes I did. I told Howard Thiesen I was
interested several times.

BUD WISEMAN
Why did you think you were qualified
for that position?

CAROLYN BARTELL
I was better qualified. I've been with
the company longer, I have a larger field
of experience, and have a vast
knowledge of Phases 1 and 2 from
working on the car programs. I have
been a Supervisor and a General
Supervisor; I've implemented the Four
Phase Process successfully and have

done a better job.

BUD WISEMAN
Did Howard Thiesen know this?

CAROLYN BARTELL
Yes. I gave him my entire work history
and my resume.

The next person to be called was Karen Dawson. She
was escorted into the room.

BUD WISEMAN
How long did you spend with the lawyer
hired by General Motors before today's
deposition?

KAREN DAWSON
About an hour and a half.

BUD WISEMAN
I understand that you work part time?

KAREN DAWSON
Yes, I do. About thirty hours per week.

BUD WISEMAN
How long have you been doing this?

KAREN DAWSON
Three years now.

BUD WISEMAN
And you worked for Howard Thiesen

during part of this time?

KAREN DAWSON
Yes.

BUD WISEMAN
What were your duties?

KAREN DAWSON
I worked on future product planning and
on the business plan.

BUD WISEMAN
And did you work with Ellen Blend on
the business plan?

KAREN DAWSON
Yes, I did.

BUD WISEMAN
Why was it that you left working for
Howard Thiesen?

KAREN DAWSON
He told me that if I didn't work for him
full-time by December 1, of 1993, I was
a voluntary quit.

Many other women were deposed that day including
Amy Templin and Lisa Berkstrom. Amy clearly stated
that she and other women were held back from
promotion by Howard Thiesen. Lisa was afraid of
hurting her position and would not say anything that
would benefit my case. Nor would she admit to having
taken a leave of absence due to being upset with Clayton

O'Connor's mismanagement of her. She obviously took the instruction of General Motors' attorney seriously and did nothing to flower my position.

A short break again took place and the next person to be deposed entered the room. Marcie Moran sat down and the questioning continued.

>MARCIE MORAN
>I'm forty-four years old.

>BUD WISEMAN
>And your education?

>MARCIE MORAN
>I've taken classes at U of D Mercy.

>BUD WISEMAN
>Do you feel you were treated unfairly in the Strategic Planning Group?

>MARCIE MORAN
>Yes.

>BUD WISEMAN
>What happened?

>MARCIE MORAN
>I was a Program Timing Manager and had five car divisions to support. I was told I would be given some help, but I never was.

She began to well with emotion.

When I said I needed to have some help,
they put me under another timing
manager and gave my job to Clayton
O'Connor.

Her emotion was building.

And then they promoted him into the job
to a managerial level and gave him an
immediate assistant to help him.

Now the tears were coming forth. It had been a very
emotional issue with her for many years now.

BUD WISEMAN
And how did you feel about that?

MARCIE MORAN
I feel I was raped by the corporation.
I'll never get over that!

Everyone in the room stirred.

BUD WISEMAN
Did you ever have an opportunity to
work with Clayton O'Connor?

MARCIE MORAN
Yes.

BUD WISEMAN
How did people that worked for him feel
about him.

MARCIE MORAN
His nickname was 'Polaroid' because he
was always so negative!

The next person to be called was Ronald Northrup. Ron
was one of five men who were demoted in the Quality
Department. He wore a broad smile and was a jolly sort
of man. He had rosy cheeks, and a reverberating
personality. He was seated, now, and being questioned.

BUD WISEMAN
And you were one of five gentlemen
who were demoted about the same time
as Ellen Blend?

RONALD NORTHRUP
Yes, I was.

BUD WISEMAN
And you now have a position with the
Timing Group at a lower level?

RONALD NORTHRUP
That's right.

BUD WISEMAN
Did you seek any legal action for what
was done to you?

RONALD NORTHRUP
No, I didn't.

BUD WISEMAN
And why was that?

RONALD NORTHRUP
I figured somebody would take 'em to
the cleaners.

A few people stirred in their chairs and
the questioning continued.

BUD WISEMAN
It is true that men do not hold an equal
position in matters of this sort. Please
state in your own words how you were
told that you were being demoted.

RONALD NORTHRUP
I was told that us ol' guys would have to
move over for the young ones to come
in.

A break took place, and Bud Wiseman and I walked
down the hallway; we were on our way to one of the
offices that we used to review notes and discuss what
had been said. As soon as we were out of sight, he took
both of his hands, firmly placed them on my shoulders
bracing me. He then danced me around in a circle and
stated, *"Isn't it great theatre!"*

After the break, everyone re-entered the conference
room and was seated. The next person called was John
Nelson.

BUD WISEMAN
Did you spend some prior time with
General Motors' attorney before today?

JOHN NELSON
Yes, about an hour, two months ago.

BUD WISEMAN
Did you ever work with Marcie Moran?

JOHN NELSON
Yes I did. I worked with her when she was pulled off of a car program and replaced by Clayton O'Connor.

BUD WISEMAN
What did you think about that?

JOHN NELSON
I thought it was unfair.

BUD WISEMAN
Did anyone else tell you they thought their treatment was unfair?

JOHN NELSON
Yes. There were a couple of other women that thought their treatment by Howard Thiesen was unfair.

BUD WISEMAN
Since Ellen Blend was assigned to your group, were there any managerial-level positions that opened up?

JOHN NELSON
No. But a managerial-level person was placed under me.

> **BUD WISEMAN**
> Do you feel that Ellen Blend should
> have been considered for that position?

> **JOHN NELSON**
> No. It was not her discipline.

> **BUD WISEMAN**
> Did you consider her for any other
> managerial-level position in your
> department?

> **JOHN NELSON**
> No. Ellen was seen as a good entry-
> level management employee.

I was disappointed that, for such a caring man, he wore the corporate hat--as I am sure he was directed to do. He may not have done much for my personal situation, but at least he spoke well on Marcie Moran's behalf.

It was another day of depositions and Diane Hillsdale was to be deposed. She was terribly nervous and quite uncomfortable about having been called upon. Bud Wiseman put her at as much ease as he could. Her deposition was fairly insignificant as was Alex White's, also of Personnel. Next, however, Les Weaver of Personnel was called in for questioning.

> **LES WEAVER**
> Performance was not the issue. She was
> improperly classified. The work content
> and what someone brings to the job is
> what determines the level.

Bud Wiseman was leaning slightly forward in his chair.

    BUD WISEMAN
    I enter Exhibit 1, Scott Warner's
    response to Ellen Blend. It appears he is
    bitter that the effort he put forth resulted
    in this action. Despite his positive
    efforts, Robert Levin had not reviewed
    the letter with her. Did Scott Warner
    leave voluntarily?

    LES WEAVER
    Yes, it was his desire.

Bud Wiseman leaned even further forward now.

    BUD WISEMAN
    This is Exhibit II, an External
    Opportunity Program, or Buy Out
    Settlement Agreement, which includes a
    statement agreement that 'you will not
    sue the company' as part of the
    negotiated buyout. Scott Warner states
    that when he approached you regarding
    any legal ramifications that might come
    from his letter regarding Ellen Blend,
    that you told him that he had already
    signed, and had no recourse!

    LES WEAVER
    Oh, there are probably claims by Ellen
    and claims by Scott.

    BUD WISEMAN
    Is there such a documentation called

P.I.P.?

LES WEAVER
Yes, there used to be. It's a
Performance Improvement Program and
can be an addendum to the evaluation
process. It outlines the deficiencies that
a person may have and gives time
elements to see if improvements can be
made.

Bud Wiseman was really leaning in toward his deponent
now.

BUD WISEMAN
What determines if this process is used?

LES WEAVER
The supervisor decides. I couldn't see
any need for a P.I.P. in this case.
Everything was well documented. The
assumption is that the allegations are
correct.

Bud Wiseman and I walked down the sunny, tree-lined
street to lunch. I said to him, "Boy, you certainly didn't
like Les Weaver, did you?"

"How could you tell?" he asked.

"You were really leaning in to him. It was the body
language!" I said.

"You're right. He was just too pompous and I didn't
like him," he said frankly.

Back in the conference room, the next person being deposed was Don Milton.

BUD WISEMAN
How long have you worked for General Motors?

DON MILTON
Thirty years, since February of sixty-five.

BUD WISEMAN
So, you're fifty-three?

DON MILTON
Yes.

BUD WISEMAN
In what time frame did Ellen Blend work for you?

DON MILTON
I was offered the Program Management job in the summer of eighty-eight, and formed a group of about twelve people, which included Ellen.

BUD WISEMAN
Were you a part of her promotion to eighth level?

DON MILTON
Yes. There was a letter approved from

Harry Cardine. There was no HRM
meeting. It was Platform approved.

BUD WISEMAN
Were you aware of any problems
regarding Ellen Blend?

DON MILTON
All managers had problems. It was with
implementing the strategy.

BUD WISEMAN
You were in agreement with her
promotion?

DON MILTON
Absolutely. She was the best I had.

BUD WISEMAN
Were you aware of Ken Centurion's
promotion to the Timing Core position?

DON MILTON
Yes. I recommended Carolyn Bartell
for that position also. I have a high
regard for both people.

BUD WISEMAN
How did you feel about Clayton
O'Connor of your group? Did you
promote him to a managerial-level?

DON MILTON
That proved to be a mistake.

BUD WISEMAN
Why is that?

DON MILTON
Once he was promoted, he didn't feel he
had to work. And he didn't work well
with people.

BUD WISEMAN
How was that?

DON MILTON
He was very brisk and caustic, even to
me.

Don Milton went out on a limb for me and I was most
appreciative. I later thanked him, but he assured me that
he meant every word he said—I was the best that he had.
I was very shocked that a man of his position would
jeopardize his future with the corporation. I was also
sure that an attempt was made to brainwash him by the
defendant's attorney prior to his deposition. He was
steadfast in not allowing anyone to prevent him from
speaking in my behalf.

While I was grateful for his support, both he and Harry
Cardine were responsible for Marcie Moran's
mismanagement. I suspect Don Milton may have
regretted that action later.

I was still working through all of the depositions, taking
vacation time for the days I needed to appear and would
not be at work.

John Nelson stopped by to see me one day. He looked at me rather concerned and stated, "This must be very hard on you. The lawsuit, I mean."

I agreed that it was. He asked if I was available Friday about 9:00 a.m. I glanced at my calendar and said that I was. He then told me that he and I had to go down to Personnel regarding an outstanding parking violation I had when I had a company vehicle.

They finally got me. I had to pay the parking ticket— about two years later!

Carolyn Bartell stopped by my office to ask me if I had heard that there had been three heart attacks and one death in the Quality Department that year. I had not, but I knew very well that General Motors had surely been the cause and that was criminal.

As the case went on, I found that most people were not afraid to talk with me and worked very hard to support me; they continually fed me information. Still, others shied away, and were afraid for their own positions.

I was walking down the hallway after delivering some documents to another office and saw Carol Ashton, one of my previous co-workers, who had worked for Clayton O'Connor. Carol just turned her head and looked away, not responding to my greeting.

And then there was Karen Dawson, who came to my office and slipped a confidential envelope to me. "You won't believe what I found! That copy is for you," she stated, as she handed me the envelope and quickly walked away.

I opened the envelope to find paperwork which clearly stated, "Proficiency Promotion for Ellen Blend." How amazing, I thought. It had been signed by Mr. Majors, Corporate Headquarters Personnel. The corporation had evidently recommended that I be promoted back to my previous level, but my own division must have refused. This was a very interesting piece of information.

The next time that I saw Kurt Hathaway in the hallway, he pretended not to see me and looked the other way. I tried to get his attention, but he avoided my glance. Since he had accomplished getting his eighth level back, he was certainly not going to jeopardize his position by talking with me. He simply averted me. How uncomfortable he must be in his regained position.

The case was still proceeding and I continued working. My co-workers were becoming restless. Word had been running rampant with the returning deponents and I had been accumulating quite a cheering squad.

Kevin Brandt came up to me and said, "I hope what I've heard is true."

"What's that?" I asked.

He looked at me shyly and with apprehension, "That you have won your case," he said.

"No," I said. "Where did you hear that?"

"From the Design Group," he said. "You know they are pretty unhappy there, too."

I told him that I knew that they were. I also knew that they were threatening to unionize.

It wasn't a half-hour later, and Dana Patrick came to see me. "Well, is it true? Congratulations!"

Again I said "Is what true?"

"I heard that you won your case and now you're going for back pay," he said.

I loved it. Unfortunately, I couldn't confirm any of the rumors for them. The case had not been settled.

I told my friend, Gwenn, that hardly a day went by but what someone didn't come to my office to offer some information they felt would be valuable to me. I couldn't believe all the support that I was getting.

I also told her something else that I had heard. Of all the company car drivers at my division, only three percent were women. She commented, "It never was fair, was it."

Chapter Fourteen

Victory at Last

Finally, official word did come. Bud Wiseman called me at my office to tell me that the case was settled and that my hard bargaining had paid off. They also wanted me out of there—fast. They actually gave me two days to finish what I was doing and to pack up.

In his telephone call to me, Bud Wiseman explained that he would be having the check made out directly to him. He would place it in a trust account and then disburse a check to me. I said that would be fine.

Upon my exit interview, part of the new management called me in to ask what changes I would make in the organization if I were to be given the chance. I was able to hold my head up high and tell them that I would communicate better with the workforce and express more appreciation to my employees for their efforts.

Barbara Moore came to congratulate me. "You'll be hearing from me," I said. "I'm going to have a Victory Party, and you're invited!"

I wanted to thank all of the people who were so great in supporting me through the whole ordeal. I was overwhelmed at the assistance that I received. It was the least I could do to express my thanks to each and every one of them.

Barbara Moore found it better to be unavailable for my party, continuing her stance to be uninvolved. However, she did take me to dinner at a very nice club in celebration of the event and to express her continued support.

When I received the check as stated from Bud Wiseman, I deposited it into my bank through the drive-in teller window. When I returned home, there was a message from him left on my recorder. He asked that I call him as soon as I got the message.

I had just talked to him that morning, so I assumed it was probably left previously and did not return the call. The telephone rang immediately, and it was Bud Wiseman asking me why I didn't call him. "Didn't you get the message?"

I explained that I did, but that I thought we did talk.

"We did," he said. "I just wanted you to know that I released a check to you in the wrong amount. I've put a stop-payment on the check. I'll release another one to you today," he continued.

"The wrong amount?" I questioned.

"Yes. I overpaid you," he stated.

"Well, I didn't even check to see if it was the right amount. I just trusted you knew what to give me."

"Well I made a mistake. What is your account number? I'll wire the amount directly into your account," he said.

"Oh. I'll get it for you."

"I'm sorry about the mistake," he said. "It's just a little less than the amount I said that it was."

"That's okay," I said. "But you didn't have to stop payment. I would have given it back to you."

"Well, I just did. You never know with some people."

"I never checked the amount. I just trusted you had it figured right," I continued.

"You never checked it?" he asked.

"No. I told you it wasn't about money!"

It was the evening of the Victory Party and my daughter, Sue, stood at the doorway handing out long-stemmed roses to each lady and a boutonniere to each man that arrived. A waitress waited just outside the door giving glasses of champagne.

The tables were set with white table linens and people were sitting and standing, mingling and talking, until everyone arrived. I did my best to make the rounds to everyone. I welcomed them warmly and extended my appreciation for their great efforts on my behalf. I was very happy and wore a broad smile.

Bud Wiseman proudly stated, "I hardly see a person here that I haven't deposed!"

I supposed that was true.

My gentleman friend, Steve, entered the room. He got his fair share of attention due to his good looks. He really wanted to attend. He said that I was the only one he knew that had ever had a Victory Party. I welcomed him and introduced him to a few of my friends. When he was comfortable talking with people on his own, I moved on to talk with others. The room was filled with about thirty people, standing, sitting, mixing and having good conversation.

Stephanie, a co-worker, approached me and asked who that good-looking man was that she saw me with.

"Oh, that's Steve. He's the fellow I'm dating," I said.

"I heard he's a lawyer," she said.

"Yes, he is," I admitted.

"Did he help you with your case?" she asked.

"No. I never asked him to. I was already pretty far along in the case by the time I met him," I said.

"Oh, I see," she said. "Well it doesn't hurt to have too many attorneys around."

"Well, we have three here tonight," I offered.

"We do?" said Stephanie.

"Yes, Bud's assistant is here, too. I never allowed him to work on my case, but I've talked to him many times-- so I invited him."

I continued to mingle with my supporters.

"Well, I never heard of anyone having a Victory Party," said Bud Wiseman. "I'm sure glad you invited me."

"Well, you are the party!" I told him. "You did a wonderful job for me."

"Thanks. You're a very strong lady," he told me. "Herb was excited too, even though he didn't work on your case. He's always liked you."

"Well, I'm pleased to have him here," I said.

Dinner dishes were picked up and dessert was served. I returned to my table to find that a selection had been made for me from a variety dessert platter.

I turned to Steve and asked, "Where did this come from?"

"I put it there for you," said Steve.

"Oh, thanks! How did you know that I love caramel?"

"Somebody here told me," he said.

"Well, how nice. They're all such great friends, aren't they?" I said.

"I should say. It's a great party."

Shortly after the new year was my birthday. I was accompanied by my children and some friends for a celebration at By-the-Bay, where I had held my Victory Party. Upon entering the dining room, my eyes met a familiar smiling face, and I returned the smile as I passed him.

When I reached my table, I realized who had given me that cunning smile. It was Les Weaver from Personnel. I reflected on his facial expression. What I read was, "You got us, smart lady!"

As time went on, I returned to General Motors many times to perform independent contract work for various divisions. On one of my assignments, I found that Alex White, also of Personnel, had been transferred to the division in Pontiac where I was currently working. At each instance of meeting my confident gaze, his head dropped and his eyes met the floor. How proud I felt not to have been defeated.

And, although unconfirmed, the last I heard was that Howard Thiesen, who previously had a staff of fifty people when I worked for him, had been transferred to Flint to manage six people, all of whom are men.

Victory at last.